You *Can* Make This Sh*t Up!

stories, plays and other lies

Gwyn McAllister

This book dedicated to _____
(this space available in subsequent
printings for a small fee*)

*$200 OBO

Contents

short STORIES

* Hmmm?.....(A Mystery) 3
* The Emissary...11
* No Matter How You Looked At It –
  He Was Still Dead.. 25
* Czarina Zofia 43
* Overrated Is An Understatement 47
* The Correspondence of H.H. and L.L.............. 53
* Nothing But The Truth.................................... 57

short PLAYS

* Happy Birthday.. 67
* Pizza Rat.. 93
* (I'm Dreaming Of) A White Plains Christmas 115
* The Understudy – A Broadway Murder
  Mystery 127
* Somewhere in the Bronx................................. 155
* The Other Side...175
* December 27th...199
* Fiction 221

Poems

* Top of the Food Chain Blues...........................241
* Walter...245
* Octopalypse... 249

"I won't let my bi-polar disorder slow me down."
[or speed me up, unless I'm under deadline]
—Abilify commercial

short STORIES

✳ Hmmm?.....(A Mystery)

Jesus was scratching at my shoulder. He woke me up out of a deep sleep. Jesus is my cat. (It's pronounced the English way – Jesus – not the Spanish Jesús.) I usually just call him Jeezy. It annoys me when people think I'm saying Cheesy. That would be a stupid name for a cat – or for anything for that matter – except perhaps a cheese-based product.

Luckily it was Sunday and I didn't have to get up right away. I had a hell of a headache. Just lifting my head from the pillow caused enough pain to make me want to stay in bed all day. I'd finished off most of one of those big bottles of wine the night before, while crying over my favorite movie *In Cold Blood*. I've always felt so sorry for Perry. I mean, sure, it must have sucked for the Clutter family, but think of poor Perry – limping to the scaffold. He wasn't a bad guy. Just got led astray by that asshole Dick. And I've always liked Robert Blake, even if he did kill his wife.

My throbbing head eventually forced me to crawl out from under the covers so I could grab some aspirin. After downing a handful I decided to stay up and make coffee.

Since I had no plans – and absolutely no inclination – to go anywhere, I just grabbed the clothes that I had tossed on the floor the night before and started to get dressed. On top of being completely rumpled, my tee shirt and jeans were also spotted with stains. Oh, well, I thought, nobody's gonna see me. I might as well wear them again before I throw them in the wash. Then I noticed that the staining was pretty extensive – random spots and splotches all over both the grey tee shirt and the jeans. What the hell? And what *is* that? It's not wine. I examined the clothes closely. Looks like blood, I thought. Am I bleeding? *Was* I bleeding? I checked myself over. Nothing. Could have been a bloody nose I guess, but you'd think I would have noticed that, even while profoundly compromised by alcohol. I threw the clothes back on the floor and put on some sweat pants and another rumpled tee shirt.

I didn't give it that much thought. At the moment getting some caffeine into me was the priority. Anything to ease the pain. I checked the news while drinking two cups of coffee, then headed to the bathroom to brush my teeth. That's when I remembered the stained clothing. Toothbrush sticking out from the side of my mouth, I grabbed the tee shirt and jeans from the bedroom floor and took a closer look. The stains sure looked like dried blood. I guess it could have been something else and, even so, waking up to bloody clothes isn't the worst thing that can happen to someone. I mean, turn on the news. The world is spontaneously combusting. And celebrities I've never heard of are getting arrested.

Nothing much of note happened – in either *my* world or the world at large – for another month. Then one morning – again a Sunday – I discovered my discarded clothes covered with stains again. This time I examined them more thoroughly. The stains were definitely blood – some a dark red, some older – more brownish. I touched one of the fresher looking spots on the tee shirt. It was still a little damp. I dropped the shirt, horrified. Oh my God! I must have killed someone in my sleep!

That's the only possible explanation. The blood wasn't mine. I had ruled that out. I found Jesus and checked him over for wounds but his long orange fur was completely clean. I even looked at the bottom of his paws and between his toes. Nothing. Murder! It had to be. Well, maybe my victim survived, but clearly I had violently attacked someone while in a semi-conscious sleepwalking state.

OK now. No need to panic. There could be some sort of reasonable explanation. I've never sleepwalked in my life. Why would I start now? And where's the murder weapon? Huh? Answer that one. I checked out all the kitchen knives. None looked bloody but, I suppose if I could get dressed, leave my apartment, hunt for victims and kill them in my sleep, I could also wash a knife. I certainly must have washed my hands. Oh my God! The detectives always check the sink traps and spray that stuff all around that makes the blood residue light up like a big neon GUILTY sign.

I thoroughly sanitized the kitchen and bathroom with bleach, pulled apart the plumbing from both sinks and cleaned the pipes inside and out. Now for the bloody clothing. The evidence from the previous murder was still in the laundry basket. I grabbed both sets of clothes and headed out the door. I spent a couple of hours traveling around to different neighborhoods, looking for dumpsters and trash cans in out of the way places. I buried one item in each of four different receptacles. I know all about the disposing of evidence. I read a lot of true crime.

For the next few days I checked out every single local news source I could think of, searching for stories about unsolved murders. I wasn't sure what I was looking for exactly, but none that I found seemed like a good fit. Then again, this is New York City. Only the most sensational crimes make the news. Good thing the cops haven't picked up on any of the similarities between the two murders. They don't yet know that they've got a serial killer on their hands. But does two murders make me a serial killer? I think it's three or more. I looked it up. I was right. As long as I stopped at two I might very well get away with it.

And maybe there *are* no similarities between the murders. Do I have an MO? Not even sure who my victims are. Are mine revenge killings of people I know and hate? Are the victims random strangers? Men? Women? A combination? Do I have a type? Old? Young? Children? Not children! I couldn't do that. Of course it's not children, that would have made the news.

Or maybe I'm an avenger – ridding the world of bad people – like Dexter – or Raskolnikov. Or maybe I'm just trying to prove my superiority like Leopold and Loeb.

I suppose it's possible that I haven't *killed* anyone – just wounded two people. Stabbed and ran. That was a lot of blood though. And I'd know better than to leave any witnesses. Witnesses! Am I cornering people in dark alleys, or following them home, or breaking into apartments? So many questions.

For example, was I wearing gloves? Oh, no! I hope I was. I probably was careful like that. I kept a box around for cleaning up. Chances are I wore a fresh pair each time and then buried them in a dumpster afterwards. But what if I wasn't? I started sleeping with gloves on.

The next murder occurred a mere two weeks later. The time between kills always decreases as the sociopathic murderer develops a tolerance and needs his fix more often. And now, with three victims, I truly was a serial killer. A rare breed – a female serial killer!

This time it was a Saturday when I awoke to the familiar pile of bloody clothes. I only stalk on the weekends apparently. Makes sense. But NO! None of this makes sense. I'm not the type. But they never are.

Checked the news once again. Nothing. Am I disposing of the bodies in such a way that they haven't been found? How? That would certainly involve chainsaws and taxis – neither of which I've ever been very comfortable with.

The cops are probably intentionally covering up the story so as not to create a panic situation. The good news is – they must not have any witnesses or there'd be an artist's rendering circulating. No need to think of disguises yet.

What name will the media give me? I spent more time than I should have giving that question considerable thought. Since I didn't even know my mode of killing, it was difficult to come up with an appropriate nickname. The only common denominator that I was aware of was the day of the week. Even though my latest murder happened on a Friday night – it was probably technically Saturday. So – how about the Saturday Stabber? Stabber? That sounds so lame. Not vicious enough. The Saturday Slasher is much better but I don't know if I'm stabbing or slashing – or maybe slitting throats. If only I knew

The bloody clothes! Luckily I hadn't raced out to dispose of them right away this time. I spent hours examining the stains, researching blood spatter identification online. The spots didn't seem to fit the criteria for either stabbing or slashing very clearly. No signs of arterial spurting, trace misting or obvious cast-off splatter. As far as I could determine the stains all appeared to have been caused by contact transference. Looking closely, some of the spots vaguely resembled familiar objects, but I couldn't quite identify them. Could this be a clue? Probably not, and probably not the best use of my time.

I finally decided on the nickname The Queens Creeper – vague enough, but still ominous.

Should I send a cryptic letter to the police? I considered all of the pitfalls of such an undertaking and how I could avoid them. Make sure the paper and ink can't be traced, be wary of leaving any DNA, mail the letter far from my own neighborhood. What I should have spent more time considering was what I could possibly say in the letter to prove that I was, in fact, the murderer and not just some nut job seeking attention. I didn't know anything about my own murders. Never mind the kind of details that only the killer would know. I didn't even have a clue as to the basics – location, method, not even who my victims were. This was going to be a very challenging case. I would have to work backwards. I knew the identity of the murderer but nothing else. And I better work fast – faster than the police.

Unfortunately, I had no idea where to start. I began to panic. I discovered that people actually do wring their hands in times of extreme stress. I also did a lot of pacing and even tried some hair pulling. I was starting to lose it. I felt like Lady MacBeth or the protagonist of *The Tell Tale Heart*. Have I gone mad? I felt like screaming, "Here! Here I am! Arrest me officers. I can take it no longer."

The feeling passed. I ate lunch.

That night, getting ready for bed, I thought about when I might strike again. There would probably be only one week between murders this time. Next Saturday. Or Friday. Or maybe even Sunday night. I should think of some way to prevent any further bloodshed. Tie myself to the bed? Set a booby trap somehow? Have a friend stay over? But what would I tell that friend? And do I really want an overnight guest? Well, I have time to think it all through. At least a week. And maybe I'm done at three. Probably.

I slept well and woke up refreshed, earlier than usual, and no longer insane. As a matter of fact, I was in quite a good mood. Until, that is, I spotted something on the floor. Lying on top of my discarded clothes in fact. A dead pigeon. Really dead. He (or she) was headless. It was an unnerving sight. My God! I'm biting the heads off pigeons in my sleep.

Before I had time to recover from that shock, the cat flew into the room, snatched the decapitated bird in his mouth and jumped through the window onto the fire escape.

Jesus was the Queens Creeper!
And he was getting deadlier by the day.

✱ The Emissary

I

I woke up this morning and found that I had turned into a cockroach. Not a huge cockroach like Gregor Samsa – just an ordinary sized cockroach with all of the usual cockroach attributes. Now you might think that I saw this as catastrophic, but my life wasn't entirely satisfactory – far from it actually – and I welcomed the change. I scurried (scuttled? scampered? – I'm still adjusting to my new terminology) out of bed and ran to the kitchen – of course. Luckily, the former me – the human version – was very messy so there was plenty to eat. As a human I had lived alone and was lonely much of the time. In my latest incarnation I share my home with many, many friends. We're not worried in the least about running out of food since our life expectancy is only about one year. As long as the exterminator doesn't pay us a visit, or someone stomps on me – I believe I will now enjoy a happy life.

II

Like most New Yorkers I used to complain about how small my living space was. Now, as a three quarter of an inch long insect, my apartment seems huge! It takes me about the same amount of time to walk from one end to the other, as it previously took for me to walk to Central Park – 10 blocks away. Not to mention, that I can now walk on walls, which makes every CUBIC foot count. With 9 foot high ceilings, this apartment is something like 3,000 cu ft! What luxury. Walking vertically is pretty great by the way. It just takes some getting used to.

III

I have a boyfriend! His name is Norm and he spotted me on day one – when I was the new girl. I had no reference point from which to determine if I was attractive as a cockroach but apparently, according to Norm, I'm beautiful. Yesterday we had sex for the first time. I'm thoroughly smitten. Oh, wait, uh, hold on, right, OK. Someone just told me that there is no such thing as a "relationship" in the cockroach world and they also mentioned that Norm was, at this very moment, having sex with my new best friend. Well, some things in the cockroach world are very different from those in the human world, some not so much.

Update, Norm just walked up to me and introduced himself as if we had never met. He said, "Hi I'm Norm, you must be new. You're beautiful!"

IIII

I now spend my days exploring my apartment, with new cockroachy eyes. Of course, the purpose is ostensibly to look for crumbs but the amazing thing is that, now that I can crawl into every nook and cranny, I've found things of mine that I've been searching for for months! Granted, these things are of no use to me now but at least I no longer have to harbor the nagging suspicion that perhaps the super was letting himself in while I was out and had made off with a) my black beaded tank top b) my big spatula (I had to make due with the tiny spatula from the spatula set for over a year) c) my sunglasses d) the library book that I swore to the staff I had never even heard of and e) the left mate to my favorite pair of shoes. The super is completely exonerated. BTW – the spatula was behind the toilet – go figure.

ＴＨＬ

I was reprimanded. Apparently I've been breaking a lot of the cockroach rules – sleeping late, shirking my duties, eating too much, hiding when there's a group job or a meeting, gossiping and bad mouthing my fellow roaches. I was told that I have to lose my filthy human habits and shape up. I was worried about what my punishment might be – lock up, banishment, caning, death – probably death I surmised. But no, the cockroach justice system is not SO bad. For every time I don't do my share of the work I have to do 25 push ups. Hiding is punished by being pushed over onto your back so that you have to struggle to flip yourself over.

I couldn't manage to right myself the first time (I have to admit – I've been busted for hiding more than once) but the other roaches helped me back up. This cockroach life is not as easy as I had imagined. There's no chance to try to explain away your bad behavior by claiming that you're going through a tough time or you think you're getting a migraine. That shit don't fly in the cockroach world. I wanted a break from the boredom of my former life, but this cockroach business is hard work. The roaches had given me some time to adjust but now I'm expected to pull my weight – literally. This is going to take some adjustment on my part.

⊞ -I

A meeting was called yesterday. The subject – building a nest for the upcoming crop of new babies. The decision was made to tear apart and plunder my new down jacket for the project. I objected strenuously. "Can't y'all just use the old jacket from the pile of clothes I was going to donate to the Salvation Army?" No, I was told, the new jacket is made of superior material. "I know!" I said, "That's why I paid what I did for it." I never spend money on clothes but I had coveted that jacket for months before I finally broke down and bought it. And I took very good care of my prized possession – there was only one cigarette burn. That hole apparently provided access for my fellow roaches to climb in and scope out the organic down to determine that it was the best choice for the nest. I have to admit, I threw a temper tantrum, but to no avail. At least the gang didn't insist that I take part in the deconstruction process. It would have broken my heart. Instead I hid under a discarded sock and seethed for a day. Eventually one of my cockroach pals found me. She had managed to make a tiny comforter from a bit of the jacket. She draped it over me and tucked in the edges. I slept very soundly last night.

卌 -II

"Let's go to the swimming hole!" This invitation came from Violet, who's a bit of a rebel. She and a couple of the guys were planning an illicit visit to a place that is forbidden. "I'm not sure. I'm already in enough trouble," I responded, knowing full well that I wouldn't be able to resist the temptation to see this fantastic place they spoke. Off we went – to my bathroom! We all clambered up the side of the toilet and before I could issue a warning the three of them had jumped in. "Come on in!" they urged. "Uh no. I can't swim."

"Of course you can. All roaches can swim."

With some difficulty, the three made their way back up the slippery slope of the toilet bowl and prepared to jump back in. Violet grabbed my leg to try to get me to join them for a second plunge. "Looks dangerous," I offered.

"That's what they say and there are some horror stories about previous disasters – whirlpools sucking roaches under – but I don't believe it."

"Um," no thanks.

"Hey, you must know what humans use this thing for," said Jerome.

I didn't have the heart to tell them. "Uh. We wash our faces in it."

卌-|||

Some excitement today. There was a loud insistent knocking on the door. It was the police – doing a Welfare Check. We all scurried away and hid. Then, bam! The door was kicked in, which was a bit excessive and entirely unnecessary since I never lock my door. The cops looked around expecting (hoping?) to find my human corpse lying about somewhere. One cop noted that it looked like the place had been ransacked. Apparently he wasn't given a heads up. My apartment always looks that way. Eventually they left – to our vast relief. "What was that all about?" asked one of my roach pals. I guess I've been missing in human form for about a week now. Apparently someone actually took note of my absence. That gave me a warm and fuzzy feeling. Although warm and fuzzy is much more of a human state of mind. For cockroaches a good feeling is more like slick and slimy. Either way, the intrusion not only provided a distraction, but made me feel loved and needed. Just wishful thinking I suppose, It was probably the landlord who reported my disappearance – wondering why I hadn't paid the rent. Glad I belong to a real community now. Don't miss the human world at all. Well, maybe a little.

"No. Like Africa or New Guinea." Blank stare. "They're countries. Well, Africa may or may not be a continent and I'm not sure exactly what New Guinea is. But it's a huge world out there. With lots of different people and different cultures."

"Have you ever been to Africa or New Guinea?" I was asked.

"No, but I could go if I wanted to."

"Have you ever been to an apartment on the fifth floor?"

"No."

"Why not?"

"I can't just walk into someone else's apartment, even if they left the door unlocked."

"Uh. Yeah you can. You can now. I do it all the time and let me tell you something – there are entirely different people and cultures up there too."

"Not so different."

"Yeah. The apartment in the rear is totally different. It's much cleaner than here. It smells like vanilla and there's much better food – healthier."

"If you like it so much on the fifth floor then why don't you just move up there?"

"Why don't you move to Africa?"

"This is my home. Where I was born."

"Exactly!"

I've always thought I had some talent for debating but these cockroaches are smarter than I would have previously given them credit for.

𝍸 - 𝍸 - I

A special meeting was called for today. I overslept and when I walked in all eyes were on me. It was disconcerting to say the least. "What? I mean I'm sorry I'm late." There was a short awkward silence.

After clearing her throat, one of the elders began, "Have you ever wondered why you turned into a cockroach?" Actually, I had never given it much thought so I just shrugged my shoulders. She continued. "We liked you. And we felt sorry for you. You seemed so lonely. We thought you'd enjoy being part of a family. But I don't think you can change your human ways."

"I'm trying. Really I am," I responded, although I knew that was a lie.

"I'm sorry but you're lazy, argumentative and insubordinate. And now you refuse to serve the one and only cockroach

All of this emotion led to a huge group hug, which, for a human witnessing it, would have been a terrifying spectacle to behold. But for a cockroach – it was beautiful.

𝍤𝍤 - 𝍤𝍤 -𝍤𝍤

I woke up the next morning, feeling particularly cozy, so cozy in fact, that I rolled back over to enjoy a few more minutes of sleep. Then I thought better of it. Today was the day I was going to prove my cockroach worthiness. I sat up and quickly realized why I was feeling so unaccustomedly comfortable. I was in my bed, snuggled under the covers. I looked myself over. I ran my hands over my body. I was back to my human self – my fleshy, flabby, pasty, wingless, exoskeleton-less, slow and clumsy human form. It would have been tempting to just duck back under the covers and stew in self pity but I was feeling hungry so I got up to get something to eat.

The milk was sour. So much for coffee. I toasted a Pop Tart and gobbled it greedily. Before I was quite through, I purposefully left a few crumbs and a bit of raspberry filling on the plate and set it on the kitchen counter. Just in case.

I started to explore. Everything was as messy as ever and now my apartment seemed more cramped than before and everything in it so small and insignificant. As a cockroach I could spend an hour just examining every crack and crevice of my hair dryer, or I could entertain myself by climbing up and down a lampshade. Now it all just seemed so dull and commonplace.

Perhaps I had just dreamt the whole thing. Of course – that's all. I had recently had cockroaches on the brain because they had seemed to be everywhere of late. I had even called in the exterminator and made an appointment.

But it had all seemed so real. Well, I can surely find some proof that it was just a dream. I went to the bathroom and poked around behind the toilet. Sure enough, there was my spatula. But then, it's possible that during the night I just remembered putting it there. Of course, that explains that. I was just dreaming.

I decided to go out and replace the milk. I grabbed my coat, but in putting it on, I noticed a bunch of fluff was sticking out of the small cigarette hole on the front. That's nothing all that unusual, I thought. But then I saw that there was a small strip of fabric missing from the bottom. It looked like it had been ripped out – rather messily. Damn. My new coat. I must have caught it on something and torn it without realizing.

When I got back from the store, I turned on the coffee maker. Then, out of the corner of my eye I noticed something. Sure enough, it was a cockroach – just hanging out on the plate from my Pop Tart – It seemed to be looking up at me. Now this was not the kind of cockroach behavior I was accustomed to. They usually scurry off as soon as I enter a room. This one just stood there facing me. Could it be? "Violet?" I said out loud. She just kept looking at me, then bowed her head a bit and headed off to the sink. Thanking me for the snack? No. Maybe? Not sure. I cancelled the exterminator's visit and felt much better than I had in years about my day ahead.

❋ No Matter How You Looked At It – He Was Still Dead

I took the apartment with a dead body hidden within the wall because it was cheap. Not just Manhattan cheap, but it-must-be-a-scam cheap. That was because it stunk. Because of the dead body behind the wall. Which nobody knew about, including me – at first.

The ad promised a large one bedroom in a doorman building with high ceilings, walk-in closet, and views. Views! According to the listing, there was one problem that would be explained to the prospective tenant upon inquiry.

What kind of problem could possibly outweigh all of those amenities? Rose, the realtor explained the situation over the phone. There was some unidentifiable, unlocatable stench that might possibly be owing to a sewage problem – or dead rats.

Of course I had to see for myself so I made an appointment to tour this dream apartment. How bad could the smell be?

OK," said Rose, as she prepared to unlock the door. "Don't say I didn't warn you." No warning could possibly have been sufficient. The apartment smelled like Satan's laundry bag – on a particularly humid day in hell. I'm not sure if this is even possible, but it smelled kind of maggoty too. Festering is the word that comes to mind. There was definitely something festering in there. I held my breath and stepped inside.

"I'll wait out here," said Rose, clipboard covering her face. "Take your time."

"I can deal with this. I can deal with this," I kept repeating to myself as I struggled not to gag. This luxury apartment was beyond the wildest dreams of an upwardly mobile Petco cashier like myself.

At the price it was renting for, I had been fully prepared to find a tiny broom closet sized space filled with one of those yellow commercial mop buckets and a cannister of roach spray but, instead, I stepped into a real apartment, with a bathroom, a kitchen and – a bedroom, my bedroom!

I almost swooned – overwhelmed by a combination of the thought of this golden opportunity and, of course, the noxious fumes. I was ready to move in asap.

"So," began Rose, "We haven't been able to rent it for obvious reasons but the super is looking into potential sources of the smell so it will most likely be a non-issue eventually and we'll be able to rent it at market rate. However, if you're willing to take it as is now, we can offer you a two year lease at the discounted price.

Two years would be amazing, even if I did have to relocate after that. And, chances are, I'd be living in a stink-free apartment for most of that time. Once the problem had been resolved.

There's one other thing," said Rose. "You should know that the previous tenant died in the apartment. It was a suicide. His body wasn't discovered for over a week so, of course, the odor was overpowering at that time. We thought that was the only problem and it would eventually subside. But it didn't so – there you are."

A potentially vindictive ghost and unearthly mysterious odors. Not a problem. I was anxious to hand over the first, last and deposit right then. Possible curses be damned.

"Are pets allowed?" I asked, planning on hiding my dog in my luggage somehow if the answer was no. But luckily I wouldn't have to sneak Zero in and somehow muffle her barking. The building was indeed pet friendly. Of course it was. It was perfect in every way. Except for one. That one exception being obvious even in the hallway where I held a pen poised to sign my new lease.

"You sure?" asked Rose, making a questioning face. "Absolutely." "Well, not so quick. The deal is, I'm having prospective tenants spend one night in the apartment before allowing anyone to sign a lease. Only one other person even got that far and he dropped out after the trial, so..."

"No problem, I'll sign right now, write a check for the full amount, make it official. I can live with it."

"Nope. The test isn't for your benefit. I've had people back out on perfectly problem-free places after signing on. It's a huge hassle and a lose-lose all around. You've got to spend the night before you get the lease."

This prerequisite had the not-so-unpleasant appeal of a haunted house movie scenario. Spend one night alone in an abandoned miasmic apartment and the prize is all yours. I was up to the challenge.

I ran home, packed a bag, grabbed Zero and prepared for my night in the luxury sewer. How bad could it be?

When I returned, the smell was even worse, if that's possible. Zero didn't seem to mind. Dogs love stink after all. She Roomba'ed around the entire place, inspecting every corner, before settling down on the sleeping bag I had spread out in the living room.

Meanwhile I busted out a bag full of every imaginable kind of odor disguiser – room freshener, candles, diffuser sticks, incense, plug-ins and some sort of electronic device that claimed to suck up odor and turn it into ultra-hydrolicized anti-oxidant air – whatever that is. When I asked the hardware store clerk if it really worked, she said, "Who knows? I have other customers to deal with. Do you want it or not?" That was enough of an endorsement for me.

I tried to imagine my life in this Manhattan abattoir. Clearly I could never have a guest. OK. My sex life wouldn't suffer much. The only men I "dated" were the types that you most definitely did not bring home, or ever give your address to.

I tried to picture enjoying a meal here. Impossible. But – the building had both a beautiful lounge and a rooftop deck. Naturally. Would the smell linger on my clothes so that people would avoid me and I'd very possibly get fired from my job? I didn't think so. And Petco could always move me to the warehouse if necessary. So, what's the issue – you surely must get used to the smell. Problem solved. Or so I thought.

Eating, entertaining and social alienation weren't the only obstacles to overcome, as I soon found out. Trying to fall asleep in a space that olafacorily outdistanced a Port-a-Potty on a construction site was much more challenging than I would have thought. I had brought an air mattress and plenty of comfortable bedding and I'd always been a sound sleeper. It's just that anytime I would try to shut off my brain in preparation for unconsciousness, the smell took over. Plus, in trying to switch positions, the clothespin that I clipped on my nose as a final precaution kept getting knocked off. It can't be healthy to breath through your mouth all the time anyway. So I ditched that idea and tossed and turned for about two hours.

I was about to give in to my final resort and start swigging from a bottle of Nyquil when I realized that Zero wasn't curled up in bed with me as she always was. I called. No response. I pushed myself up off the floor and went searching for her. Finally I found Zero hanging around the side of the refrigerator. She was whining and scratching away at the wall. Seemed like even she had had enough and was looking for an exit. I tried pulling her away a couple of times but she was relentless. She was desperate to get behind that wall. "That's probably where the dead rats are," I thought. "I'll let the super know – once I've signed the lease that is." Until then it was most definitely not to my advantage to reveal the source of the stench. A potentially easy fix would mean that the deal was off.

I pulled the refrigerator out from the wall a little ways to see if this was maybe something I could deal with myself after I moved in. That's when I noticed a fresh plastering job covering up the boundaries of what looked like a giant mouse hole. "That's gotta be some huge rat that someone was trying to keep out," I thought, facetiously of course. But why had someone taken a big chunk out of the wall and then plastered the whole thing over? Only one way to find out, and I was most likely going to be up all night anyway.

I looked around for something to use to knock the hole open. What could I possibly find in an empty apartment? Then I remembered the air hydrolocizer, which was quietly humming away in the living room as it churned out super oxidized air. "Good thing I bought this," I thought as I starting smashing away at the wall with the shoebox sized instrument. Zero was barking enthusiastically while I worked up a sweat slamming the surprisingly solid box at the wall over and over again. Finally the drywall section gave way. I pushed it all the way into the crawlspace and peered in, expecting to find an entire village of dead rats.

But there weren't rats. No even a single one. What there was was a rotting human corpse. The body was set back a little way from the wall, lying flat on its back with its hands by its sides, like a dead person in a coffin, only there was no coffin and the deceased guy was wearing jeans and a "Stay Calm and Carry On" tee-shirt, and he didn't look the least bit peaceful.

You might think that I would have reeled back in horror at this point, but instead I climbed right through the rat hole and took a closer look. It was part curiosity, and part excitement that I had potentially just discovered the solution to my problem. I felt like I had just pried open the golden door and found the remains of King Tut. This was a life changing discovery. Never mind that some poor soul was likely murdered in this apartment and stuffed into a crawlspace. His tragedy was my salvation. All I had to do was get rid of the body and I'd sleep like a baby in my luxury apartment for the next two years. But not yet. The decomposing corpse would have to stay for now.

In the meantime, there was no reason to spend the night there, gagging on putrefaction. I grabbed Zero (who had somehow snuck into the makeshift mausoleum and was yanking away at a sleeve that I feared – not unreasonably – might lead to the detachment of an arm), propped the piece of wall back into place, pushed the fridge back and headed out the door.

Zero and I spent the next few hours at an all night diner, celebrating our morbid find. Around six am, we headed back to the apartment. This time when I opened the door, I inhaled deeply and reveled in the repulsive odor that was about to earn me the deal of a lifetime. By nine I was showered, dressed refreshed and ready to sign that lease.

* * * *

I moved the majority of my stuff in that very day. I still had a week left on my sublet in the outer reaches of Queens so I wouldn't have to sleep in my Manhattan mausoleum until I could figure out how to evict the current "tenant". "Should be simple," I thought.

Why would I have thought that? Disposing of a dead body is never easy, even under the best of wooded or swampy rural living circumstances. The task is near impossible when you live in an apartment building in the heart of a city and don't own a car. I tried to remember the details of every true crime book I'd ever read. Dumpster seemed to be the way to go with an urban murder. Transporting the body to a dumpster was the tricky part. Searching through the internet I discovered that body parts in a suitcase was the most popular means of dumpster disposal. I bought the largest suitcase I could find at the thrift store. OK. OK. OK. Just get the body into the bathtub.

I couldn't do it. I couldn't even fathom doing it. Not after drinking half a bottle of tequila. Not after pumping myself up with some heavy metal music. Not after stomping around the apartment waving my fist in the air and singing along. "Rip the heart out. Eat the brains. Don't let any little bit. Go to waste." Wait, are those actually the lyrics?" I felt queasy. Like I had just tried to talk myself into cannibalism, instead of just a harmless dissection. The thought of the word "dissection" made me run to the toilet. The body never made it out of the hole. The butcher knife, hacksaw and hatchet went back to the store.

It turns out that a young man had been reported missing six months previously. The cops didn't take the disappearance seriously until his friends insisted on an investigation. In the missing man's apartment they found a piece of paper with my address written on it.

Coincidentally the missing man's name was Frank. What were the odds of that?

"Who's Frank?" the better looking cop asked me. "The missing guy," I answered. "You just told me that his name was Frank." "Right. But who's the Frank you've been talking to lately? Your neighbors reported hearing you talking to a Frank at all hours of the day and night. And they say they've never actually seen anyone besides you entering or exiting your apartment."

Thinking fast I said, "Oh! That Frank! This is Frank, my dog." The less attractive cop leaned down and examined the name tag on Zero's collar. "OK. I lied," I admitted. "Well, you see, Frank is actually my imaginary friend and, as you can imagine, I was a bit embarrassed to admit..."

"Cut the crap!" barked Depp, who was even better looking when he was angry. "I suppose your imaginary friend is the one who bought those things over there." I turned around and saw that he was gesturing towards the shovel and tarp that I had purchased at one point and foolishly left in plain sight. I was planning on returning them but you know – that would have required leaving home and ..."

As if he he was in collusion with the cops, Zero had crept sneakily into the kitchen where he was found barking and scratching at the back of the refrigerator. I guess Zero was trying to help. He knew the jig was up.

"OK. OK. There's a corpse behind the wall but I swear, he was there when I moved in." The cops looked – well skeptical wouldn't accurately describe the look. Maybe incredulous. Yes, incredulous.

"Ask Rose, the realtor. She'll tell you that the apartment stunk like a decaying body before I moved in." Fortuitously Rose was right there in the hallway. Clearly this visit had been well planned. "Tell them that the body was obviously here when I moved in. The smell – remember?" "That was the sewer," said Rose. "No it wasn't! You see, it was putrefaction all along. The corpse was here behind the wall when I moved in, causing that ungodly stench." "There's never been a rotting corpse in this apartment before," said Rose indignantly. "Well except for the previous tenant who killed himself, and that one was removed *before* you moved in."

It didn't help my case that the cops had dug up the credit card info that I had recently purchased a large amount of lime and a case of Febreze

The lime was part of a plan that I had considered but abandoned out of – well, in all honesty, out of sheer laziness. I should have paid cash for those purchases. but I'm not a wily criminal accustomed to covering my tracks. I'm not wily in general.

It was all pretty incriminating. There was nothing I could do but put my hands behind my back submissively to receive the inevitable cuffing. As the cops dragged me from my apartment I said, "This will all be sorted out in no time at all and you're gonna be embarrassed about the whole thing." Rose was smirking as I was ushered down the hallway.

"No time at all" turned out to be three weeks. Three weeks of declaring my innocence behind bars and being constantly told to "Shut the hell up freak!" "Freak", I thought was pretty harsh. I was only potentially guilty of murder. How freakish is that? I guess they were referring to the entomb-ment, but surely I wasn't the only criminal living with a corpse. But maybe it's rarer than I would have thought.

And it's not like I was making things out of human skin or eating soup out of the top of the skull. The closest I came to violating my corpse was once borrowing Frank's watch until I could replace the battery on my own. But it's not like he re-ally needed to know the time and I did return it – although I couldn't quite put it back on properly because his skin was a little loose by that time. And – OK – full disclosure – once, when I couldn't find a pair of matching socks I did glance at the refrigerator wall – briefly. But I quickly realized that that would be going too far. Now, that might have been considered a little freakish but I didn't follow through with that thought.

* * * *

Luckily some canny detective work revealed that Frank had also written the name Ivan on his calendar on the date of his disappearance – Ivan being the name of the suicidal/probably homicidal previous tenant. It would seem, judging by true crime shows, that soon-to-be-murdered victims often leave clues of that sort behind. I don't think I've ever left the name of someone who I'm planning on visiting on a scrap of paper in my apartment. I do now though.

I was eventually charged with desecration of a corpse and obstruction of justice. I was able to cop a plea for nine months prison time and one year probation. My lawyer says that I'd gotten lucky. If so, it was the first time I'd ever "gotten lucky" in my life.

Oddly enough, desecration of a corpse and obstruction of justice are NOT grounds for eviction so, as hard as he tried, the landlord was not able to get me out based on my one poor decision. Not until my lease was up anyway. I'm assuming I won't get a chance to renew the lease. Of course, I won't be able to live in the apartment until after I've completed my sentence. But I intend to enjoy the three months that will be remaining to me once I get out. Considering all of the lengths I went to for that life of luxury, I think deserve some time enjoying it. Besides, I think I'll need a soft landing place by then, although jail hasn't been too bad. My fellow inmates treat me with respect, especially after I dropped a few hints that there may have some cannibalism involved in my crime.

In the meantime I've been able to sublet the apartment. The landlord tried to prevent that until he discovered that housing court could prove expensive and probably take months. For once, the law was on my side!

I'm a little concerned because apparently subletters, if they're reluctant to leave, are notoriously difficult to get rid of – unless they're dead. Ha, ha!

I don't suppose I'll receive much of a welcome home from my neighbors. It will most likely be uncomfortable living in a building where every single one of the other tenants thinks I'm insane – and possibly a necrophiliac.

Oh well. I'm really looking forward to taking full advantage of all of the amenities the building has to offer – despite the dirty looks. Sadly, Zero went to a shelter and was adopted. So it'll just be me, all alone in the apartment. I think I'll probably miss Frank. He was a good companion and, when all was said and done, kind of a comforting presence. But no matter how you looked at it – he was still dead.

✳ Czarina Zofia

From the time she was a little girl growing up in St. Petersburg in the Soviet Union, Zofia Zandofsky had been blessed with a talent for soothsaying. Once she moved to Sheepshead Bay, Brooklyn friends and neighbors found her royal lineage dubious. But all of her credentials were in order. Above the couch in her living room hung official looking documents written in Russian and featuring an impressive looking crest of arms. Zofia smoked skinny black cigarettes and favored track suits with sequins in bright colors. Despite her customary casual wear, Zofia had an air of class and privilege about her. Allegedly she was a distant relation of Rasputin. If you looked very closely at her eyes you could see the resemblance, but she almost always had on large dark sunglasses.

The Czarina told fortunes for a living. She had a good reputation and her price was right. People came from all over the five boroughs to consult with the Russian seer. She'd been doing business out of her one bedroom apartment for over 30 years.

Penelope Filcher came to see Zofia back in the 90s. She was skeptical but friends who knew that she was bored and dissatisfied with her life recommended a visit. The Czarina did not peer into a crystal ball, consult tarot cards or read palms. She simply held the hand of her subject, looked them straight in the eye and made predictions in a very direct, matter-of-fact manner.

Czarina Zofia told Miss Filcher that her last words on earth would be "I do". She would die almost immediately after pronouncing these two syllables. That was all. This was distressing news to a young woman with hopes for a future that would include marriage and children. Miss Filcher had visions of collapsing at the altar, leaving behind a disconsolate groom and an expensive feast that no one would have any inclination to enjoy.

So, despite offers from a number of quite suitable suitors, Miss Filcher remained single. She grew older and lonelier with no company in her small apartment but her parakeet Tom. One night Miss Filcher witnessed a horrific murder from her bedroom window. She reported what she had seen to the police. A suspect was arrested and Miss Filcher was subpoenaed to appear in court. "This is it," thought Miss Filcher, imagining the killer in court pulling out a concealed gun and shooting her as soon as she swore "I do" on the bible. Although Miss Filcher rather liked the drama of that scenario she was determined to avoid the fate so succinctly spelled out for her by Zofia many years before and she refused to testify.

The lonely spinster spent a year and a half in jail for obstructing justice. When she got out she became even more of a recluse than she had been previously. Her parakeet was dead. A series of bad breaks had left her broke, friendless and depressed. She became a chain smoker and rarely left her apartment.

One day she had a bit of good luck – or rather she avoided some potentially very bad luck. While driving to the pharmacy to pick up her anti-depressants a would be suicide jumped in front of her car. Miss Filcher slammed on the brakes and her car screeched to a halt just inches from the desperate young woman. However, another car rear ended Miss Filcher's Hyundai at high speed. Miraculously no one was hurt but both cars were totaled. Miss Filcher and the other driver, a man of late middle age, emerged from their cars. Dazed, they surveyed the scene – broken glass, twisted metal, leaking gasoline. The young girl was sitting where she had landed, crying, her hands covering her face, but even she had escaped unscathed. A small crowd had gathered but aside from the girl's sobs, the scene was completely, eerily silent. The badly shaken driver of the other car reached for a cigarette to calm himself. He searched his pockets for matches but to no avail. "Does anyone have a light?" he asked.

"I do,"

said he ufortunate Miss Filcher.

* Overrated Is An Understatement

When I woke up post-delivery in the maternity ward, and a nurse came in to present me with my newborn, my first thought was, "Really? Is that it? All of *that* for *this*?" I asked the nurse if she was sure it was the right baby. She laughed a little – nervously – and assured me that this was, in fact, my baby, then left me alone, a somewhat concerned look on her face.

Now I hadn't made a very good first impression with the hospital staff. There had been a bit of a scene in the delivery room. But I'm sure that I'm not the first mother in labor to scream out, "Just cut me open and get this damn thing out. Alive or dead. I don't care. Just put me out of my misery." Well, maybe I was the only one. But I'm sure I was just expressing – loudly – very loudly – what other mothers were thinking at the time.

Anyway, once I had recovered from that trauma and was feeling a little better, I held the baby and stared at it for a few minutes. Nothing. No love. No maternal feelings. Just indifference. I wanted it out of my way so that I could order lunch. Finally I put the baby down, got out of bed and snuck out of my room. I turned at the door for one last look. "This can't be mine," I thought. I crept down the hall to that baby viewing room to see what else was on offer.

I was hoping that, upon seeing my real baby, all of the hormonal juices would start flowing and I'd know right away that there had been some sort of mix up. Didn't happen. There were five or six babies lying in bassinets. Some looked a little better than mine. Some worse. But none evoked any kind of response. I scurried back to my room before anyone could tell that I'd left my baby all alone. They tend to frown upon that sort of thing – leaving babies unattended – as I would eventually learn.

The baby was right where I left it. Making some little noises which I did *not* find adorable. "Well," I thought. "I'm stuck with it." The nurse came back in to ask if I was planning on breast feeding. I shot her a dirty look as if she'd just asked if I'd like to consider a colonoscopy while I was there. "Why don't I take the baby so you can get some rest?" she suggested. I couldn't hand it over fast enough.

"Maybe it's just a matter of time," I thought. However, days went by with no change in my attitude. No emotions – besides feeling more than a little let down. This was so anti-climactic. All that build up for what? Talk about overrated.

I shared some of my thoughts with a few select friends. I approached the subject cautiously, not divulging all of my misgivings, just expressing it as a sort of mild disillusionment. The response was always the same. "You're just suffering from post-partum depression. It will pass." The problem was, I didn't feel depressed. Just annoyed. And it didn't pass.

It didn't help that my husband J.J. showed no more enthusiasm than I did. He basically just ignored the baby. Sometimes he would grudgingly hold it for a minute while I was trying to do something, but generally his attitude was like that of a parent who has given their child a pet for Christmas. "You wanted it. Now you take care of it." I don't remember either J.J. or I wanting a child. But we must have. Right?

Sometimes I could talk J.J. into watching the kid so I could run out to the store without having some sort of awkward encumbrance strapped to my body in some very unflattering manner. Inevitably I'd leave the store having remembered everything except baby food or diapers or any of the other baby necessities on my list. I'd get half way home, then turn around and go back and, more times than not, I'd get distracted by something like the surprisingly large selection of gum and I'd forget the baby items again. Possibly it was intentional. Staring at rows of chewing gum was more enjoyable than dealing with a helpless, mute human – 24/7.

It was worse when I took the baby with me somewhere in the car. You would think that after all the strapping in and fussing over belts, buckles, etc. I wouldn't forget that the baby was there. But I can't tell you how many times I arrived home and absentmindedly left it in the carseat. It usually only took a few minutes before I suddenly realized why I was feeling so relaxed and contented. "Shit, I left the baby in the car again." My first impulse was always to leave it there for awhile, but I'd mange to resist that thought. Got to be a responsible adult after all.

One time I did leave the baby in the car for almost an hour – by accident of course. A neighbor knocked on the door to let me know that I'd left an infant strapped into the back seat. I tried to look horrified. "Oh, my God!" I screamed as I ran out the door. What I really wanted to say was, "If you're so fucking concerned, why don't you take it?"

Maybe someone *will* take it. What does one have to do to have her child removed by the authorities? I started drinking heavily.

I had thought that I might enjoy the extra attention. It had been kind of fun being the pregnant woman whom people indulged and strangers started conversations with. But I eventually got tired of having to stop the stroller while people oohed and aahed and asked the same questions – over and over again. "What's its name? How old is it?" I always had to stop and think of the answer to that last one. Let's see – how long ago was it that my life came to an abrupt end? Sometimes I also forgot its name. Occasionally I just made one up on the spot to avoid the embarrassment.

I started buying mother's magazines to see if I could get inspired. Maybe if I thought of this as a hobby I'd take more of an interest. "It just takes a while to get into the rhythm of it all," my friend Veronica said to me one day. She'd said the same thing about yoga. I persisted in that case. She was wrong. And I knew better than to believe her this time.

I tried to think of something good that had come out of this whole experience. The paid time off from work was nice. Or would have been, if I could have used it to go on a vacation. I thought about asking my mother-in-law to take the baby for the remainder of my maternity leave so that J.J. and I (or better yet – just I) could go to Mexico. Veronica said I absolutely could NOT do that. "The public never forgave Princess Di for leaving her newborn to go skiing. Plus, look at what turds her kids turned out to be."

The latter argument was wasted on me. I didn't care if my kid grew up to be a turd. I didn't care if it grew up to be anything. Truth be told. I didn't care if it grew up at all.

Oh, well. I'd look terrible in a bathing suit right now anyway. I thought about ordering one of those personalized tee shirts "I went through 9 months of pregnancy and 10 hours of labor and all I got was this flabby body."

I started hanging out with other mothers. Those are the only friends you're allowed when you've got a newborn. These women were SO BORING. All they ever talked about was all of the amazing things their kids were doing. Amazing? I don't think so. Were they writing piano concertos? No. Turning over on their sides unassisted or forcing their cunning little lips into a vague semblance of a smile was more like it. God help me!

These other mothers would say thing like, "I can't wait until she can walk." or "Won't it be fun when he's talking." For myself – I can't wait until it's old enough to send off to boarding school.

And – it will be pretty great when it can support me in my old age. Sort of like a long term IRA. Except there are no guarantees. Better make it a really good boarding school.

✳ The Correspondence of H.H. and L.L.

"In the manner of a lady of antiquity sending her lover a lock of her hair," wrote Hermione, "I am enclosing a scab ripped from my body as a token of my love – more personal than the customary gift of old, as it is actually a small sample of my own life's blood." Hermione Herald, clearly a romantic at heart, sealed her letter and sent it off to Lucien Larkwood who, upon its receipt, gagged a little before tossing it into the fire. The scab sizzled unpleasantly as it burned.

"Please send me no more portions of your person," replied Lucien to his admirer. "Or further communications of any kind for that matter,"

"I received your letter and, to my great regret, I am hereby calling off our engagement," wrote Hermione in response to the terse reply of Lucien who, not only was unaware of any engagement between himself and Hermione, but had never even contemplated such an arrangement and, truth be told, barely knew her outside of their workplace

Lucien felt no need to continue the correspondence at this juncture until, that is, he received another letter. "As I have not heard back from you since I announced the dissolution of our understanding, I am obliged to inform you of the following: the great sorrow occasioned by your indifference has compelled me to take drastic action. As our union has been extinguished, so shall my life be. Sincerely, your ever faithful Hermione. PS. I am returning the pen you once lent me as well as some scrap paper I retrieved from your trash can."

Against his better judgment, Lucien picked up pen and paper (not those included in Hermione's package to him) and replied to her letter. "Absurd histrionics aside, your announcement of our disengagement has compelled me to respond to your latest missive by declaring that I am forthwith reinstating my claim to your hand and then, immediately withdrawing the offer. As you should well know, by custom it is my prerogative, as the offeree, not yours, to take any action in disfavor of an engagement!"

"I accept your offer and I reject your dismissal of same," wrote Hermione, hoping her curtness would be properly interpreted as a sign of extreme disapproval. "If you had any understanding of etiquette, you would realize that only the woman can bow out of a marital arrangement with either party's honor intact."

Lucien waited a full day before replying to Hermione. He consulted with various sources to determine who was correct as to the disengagement procedure. It seems that Hermione was the better informed of the two.

"My apologies Hermione," wrote the chastised Lucien. "For any pain I have caused you. I allowed my pride to guide my actions. I now realize that you are correct in your assertion as to proper etiquette and I plan to honor my offer of marriage."

Lucien paused in his writing at this point. He had intended to include the date that the original offer of marriage had been made but could not, despite much effort, recall the occasion at all. Regardless he sent off the apology, feeling hopeful that the misunderstanding would be resolved.

"Your letter arrived just in the nick of time," wrote Hermione in an uncharacteristically shaky hand. "After waiting for what seemed like an eternity for your reply, I had prepared a lethal potion intended to end, once and for all, my insufferable agony. The cup was actually to my lips, when the postman interrupted the execution of my desperate plan. You have – quite literally – saved my life and I will dedicate the rest of my days to repaying my debt to you with the utmost affection and obedience of – your humble servant Hermione."

Full of remorse, Lucien wasted no time at all in writing back to his stricken fiancee. "Dearest Hermione, It broke my heart to read your latest letter. Let us never again find ourselves at odds with one another. It is I, not you, who owe my life to your kindness and generosity. How could I have been fool enough to cause you any pain or uncertainty as to my fealty, or to risk losing the thing dearer to me than life itself. I will always, until my final breath, love and honor you. If only (I dare only hope) – if only – I can call you my own. Yours eternally, Lucien."

"Let us simply put aside our recent differences and make every effort to recall the pleasant times we have enjoyed together, rather than remain mired in our past mistakes," wrote Hermione, adding a less emotional – and more practical postscript. "We must make the proper announcements and set a date. I shall leave the arrangements in your most capable hands."

Although he had difficulty calling to mind any of the pleasant memories that Hermione referenced in her conciliatory letter, Lucien was still quick to answer her. "Darling, dearest, sweetest Hermione. I feel so fortunate that you are as forgiving and generous as you are. I deserve only your contempt, and yet, I am rewarded for my boorishness with nothing but sweetness and compassion from the most adorable girl in the world. How blessed I am! There is little I can do to even begin to compensate for the torture I have inflicted on you through my selfishness. Still, please accept this small token of my esteem and, if you can find it in your heart, think kindly towards – your loving Lucien."

Enclosed in the sealed and scented envelope, were three clippings of Lucien's toenails – one for each month of their courtship. Lucien had simply made a wild guess as to that figure but, as fate would have it, according to Hermione, he was exactly correct! Hermione mounted the peace offering in a silver frame engraved with hearts and cupids and this loving memento has remained ever since in its honored place above the hearth of their happy household.

✳ Nothing But The Truth

Thinking that it might be a good idea to date a convicted murderer is, in my opinion, a reasonable mistake to make. Dating a second convicted murderer, despite the catastrophic outcome of the first relationship, is – OK – just stupid. I now know this.

You're probably thinking that I must be the type of woman who trolls through those websites where prisoners advertise for pen pals. You'd be wrong. I didn't meet either of my two murderers that way. The first one I picked up hitchhiking after he'd been paroled, and the second one I met through the first one. They were cell mates at one point. It's not that uncommon to have one relationship open doors to new friendships down the line.

Now that I've explained that bit – you might have some concern that it could be dangerous to jump from the bed of one murderer to that of his murderous friend – but the truth is, my first murderer was happy to be rid of me, so there was no risk of jealousy-driven retaliation.

But why DID I date the second murderer after the first relationship went so terribly wrong? Well, hold your judgement please. Have you never fallen into the trap of dating – over and over again – the same type of person who has already proven to be absolutely the worst fit for you? How about all of those overbearing executive types, self-satisfied lawyers, unfunny stand-up comedians? We've all done it – OK? So cast no stones.

The reason I got involved in the second ex-con relationship is that, after the first break up, the second murderer said all of the right kind of gratifyingly incriminating things about the first murderer. What kind of things could he possibly have said that would have been more horrible than the fact that my ex had killed someone? Well, lots of things. The bastard apparently cheated on all of his girlfriends – including me, borrowed money from his friends with no intention of paying them back, told everyone that he served in the Army – which he didn't, and stole his sister's boyfriend's car – though even the second murderer thought that one was justified.

Learning all of these things about my ex made me really indignant. And hearing them from his friend caused me to recognize that the second murderer was sympathetic to me and, obviously, a far better person than my first murderer. He was on my side. We shared something – hatred of the first murderer. There was a connection. Also, he was very handsome. And had a scar. The first murderer was cute but the second was a definite improvement looks-wise. So I was smitten.

One thing that I hadn't really considered at the time is that murderers tend to lie. Even if they're not liars by nature, they generally have to lie after the murder – to cops, lawyers, juries, judges, etc. – so it can become habitual to them. I don't think that the second murderer was a born liar, but that doesn't really excuse him. Anyway, I later found out that all of the things he told me about his friend (except for the stolen car) were lies. They were all actually things that *he* – the second murderer – had done himself.

The second murderer may have had a few advantages over the first in terms of looks and charm – and he was very neat – almost obsessively so – but the first murderer had this going for him. He admitted to his crime – both to me and to everybody else. He confessed immediately afterwards. That's how he got paroled after only seven years. And, he came clean to me right away. He told me the whole story in the car after I picked him up at that truck stop.

It was a murder of the most excusable kind. A bar fight gone wrong – well, I guess there's really no way for a bar fight to go well. Anyway, the victim was a prick. Nobody liked him and many people, apparently, were grateful that my ex killed this asshole. At least that's what he told me and I believed him because after his release his friends were always coming up to him and slapping him on the back and telling him how glad they were to see him. A bunch of people even threw him a party at the bar where the murder had taken place and there was a big knife stuck in the middle of the cake which everyone thought was very funny. They all made the same comment, "Hey, is that *the* knife?" But it wasn't. The stabbing knife is in an evidence locker somewhere.

The second murderer (who I first met at the welcome home bar party by the way) never confessed – to me or to anyone else. He was convicted by a jury but the ruling was overthrown on appeal thanks to a good lawyer and some sloppy police work. He had been accused of killing his girlfriend. I know, I know, but apparently she was really bitchy. She was always calling him a loser and complaining that he didn't make enough money. And she was about to leave him for another man. Then she wound up dead. Shot in the head in her living room. She had told two of her friends, "If anything happens to me you know who to blame." So the friends knew – the cops knew – even her dog knew. He started growling every time he saw the murderer. Then the dog ended up dead.

The second murderer maintained his innocence from the very beginning and he swore to me that he had nothing to do with the murder. I wasn't too sure but I believe in the idea of reasonable doubt. It's the foundation of our legal system – and not such a bad principal to follow in dating either.

OK – so just bear with me on this part. It's a little hard to follow.

The first murderer was convicted of second degree murder. The second was convicted of first. I know it's a little confusing but think of it this way – I was *ASCENDING* the murder ladder with my two affairs – so the first degree murderer succeeded the second degree murderer. Got it? I guess serial killer would have been the next step but I was spared that fate, as you'll see.

Now you might think that the first degree (second murderer) sounds like he was the worst of the two. But, if you think about it, it's really the reverse because, you see, the second murderer (the girlfriend killer) had a motive. The first (the bar brawler) was just a rageaholic who could fly off the handle at any time with no provocation. The second put a lot of thought into his ALLEGED crime. Premeditation can be a good thing if you're shopping for a murderer boyfriend. It's pretty simple to stay safe. Just don't give the guy any reason to murder you. And I'm the type of person who has never given anyone a reason for even a mild scolding. So, barring my agreeing to take out a large life insurance policy (I refused *that* request), the second murderer would never have any reason to kill me.

As a matter of fact, I felt especially safe because, if anyone should know to avoid murdering someone, it would be a convicted murderer. I figured he had learned his lesson. The first murderer was the type who would have been incapable of learning a lesson. He was a hot head. The second was cold blooded. Much safer in a way. First degree murderers are far more predictable than second degree murderers. It's their nature. It's what defines them. Second degree murderers are the loose cannons of the murder world.

Obviously neither of these two murderers murdered me. But neither relationship ended well all the same. You might guess that I got beaten up or throttled by the first murderer and consequently called it quits. But that's not the case (although he did throttle me once – but I didn't pass out or anything). What happened is, he left me for the girlfriend of his victim. The bar brawl fallout. He said that he kind of owed her. Actually he owed me. Around ten grand.

The break up with the second murderer was a little more complicated. A friend of his went missing – a very attractive young woman whom he hung around with because, as he told me, she was a stylist and gave him free haircuts. There were a lot of free haircuts. After she disappeared he asked me to pretend I was the stylist and make some phone calls to her friends and coworkers explaining that I had left the country and wouldn't be coming back any time soon – maybe never. So, I did it. He had an explanation that made sense at the time but I can't remember exactly what it was. I think he told me that she was planning to make these calls herself before she left but hadn't gotten around to it and now she was somewhere that had limited cell reception – or she was at a Vipassa silent retreat. Something like that.

Well, the cops had the idea that the stylist had been murdered. And they had reason to believe that she and my boyfriend had been lovers. Since the missing woman had only one accused murderer among her acquaintances he, of course, became the primary suspect.

I became a "person of interest" because of my association with the second murderer. Plus, the detectives knew that if, in fact, a murder had taken place there had to have been a woman making those phone calls, although I thought I had done a pretty good job of disguising my voice.

Therefore, when my boyfriend asked me for $20,000 so he could fly to this foreign country where the stylist could be found and bring her back to exonerate him, what could I do? I was saving my own skin as well, right? Unfortunately, he never came back. It didn't look so good for me that I had taken a large chunk of money out of the bank the day before he disappeared. And those faked phone calls came back to bite me in the ass.

So – I'm now sitting in jail accused of conspiracy to commit murder. Yes, a body eventually turned up. In my garage as a matter of fact. Could be a coincidence. But no one seems to even be considering that possibility. The first murderer recommended that I use the second murderer's lawyer, which was a good suggestion considering the positive outcome of that case, but now I'm broke, so I'll have to take my chances with a public defender.

I *have* learned a thing or two about murder trials at this point, so that's an advantage. But, unfortunately, all of my friends and family members, who were surprisingly tolerant the first time around, eventually turned their backs on me when I got involved with the second murderer, so my only character witnesses are going to be the people from the bar stabbing party and they're mostly ex-cons. A couple of them are actually in prison right now and I heard that they might be called as witnesses for the prosecution in exchange for shortened sentences. The new girlfriend of my first murderer boyfriend offered to help me, but that ended up backfiring. She thought it would be funny to pretend to sneak a knife hidden inside a cake on a visit to me. It was the same knife from the welcome home cake so it was too big and it stuck out a little. It's kind of ironic that now that knife is in an evidence locker too.

Life is funny like that sometimes. But not so funny ha-ha right now.

short PLAYS

✳ Happy Birthday

CAST

ALEXA
JOSH
JEREMY
KATELYN
LOUIS

SCENE 1

A darkened stage. From stage left Alexa approaches. She appears to be unlocking a door and stepping inside and switching on the lights. Jeremy, Katelyn and Louis are poised to surprise her.

GUESTS (Jeremy, Katelyn, Louis)

SURPRISE!

The room is decked out for a party. Happy Birthday banner, streamers, balloons, table laden with food and a birthday cake. Guests are wearing party hats and – maybe – blowing horns. Alexa looks stunned.

GUESTS

Happy Birthday!

ALEXA

(*after a pause*) It's not my birthday.

JEREMY

Of course it is. I pulled out your paperwork last week to check on something and I noticed that your birthday was coming up – December 4th.

ALEXA

Not even close. My birthday's in May. I think December 4th might be the date I started work last year.

LOUIS and KATELYN

Jeremy!

JEREMY

I don't think I could have made a mistake like that. You must have put the wrong birthdate.

LOUIS

That's not likely. You screwed up Jeremy. Face it.

KATELYN

What a bummer. What are we gonna do with all this stuff? *(to Alexa, accusatory)* We just wanted to do something nice for you. Now it's all ruined.

ALEXA

Well, thanks. I guess. How did you guys get in?

LOUIS

We smashed a window. *(he points)*

ALEXA

Oh. Where's my cat?

LOUIS

Dunno.

KATELYN

Well this is a total drag

JEREMY

Come on. We all wanted to have a party. Let's just stay and *(shrugs shoulders)* party.

KATELYN

NO! We bought all this birthday crap. Now it's going to waste on just a party. *(disgustedly)* At Alicia's.

LOUIS

Hey, Why don't we find someone else who's having a birthday and bring all the stuff over to their place?

JEREMY

Good idea. Everybody, check on Facebook to see if any of your friends are having a birthday.

KATELYN, JEREMY and LOUIS
scroll through their phones.

KATELYN

My cousin Jonathan. *(pause)* But he lives in Wyoming.

LOUIS

Hold on. Here's somebody. Josh Feinstein.

KATELYN

Who's that?

LOUIS

I have no idea. Wait, I think I remember him now. This is a guy who was in my drunk driving class.

KATELYN

Are you friends with him?

LOUIS

Nah. The guy was kind of a loser.

KATELYN

So – do we really want to go to some loser's house?

JEREMY

Well – he probably won't be out celebrating with a bunch of friends

KATELYN

But we don't even know where he lives.

LOUIS

(looking at his phone) Bingo. He's listed in the White Pages. 222 Allen Way.

JEREMY

Let's go.

KATELYN

(reluctantly) Oh, all right. The ice cream cake's starting to melt.

They gather up all the stuff that they can carry, carelessly trashing the place, and start to leave. ALEXA is standing around – a little bit startled. They start to walk out the door, then JEREMY turns around.

JEREMY

Oh. Alicia. Do you want to come?

ALEXA

Not really.

KATELYN

This whole thing is your fault. Well, your's and Jeremy's

LOUIS

Just come.

> *Alexa puts on her coat and heads out the door
> with them, turning off the lights as she leaves.*

LIGHTS
END OF SCENE 1

SCENE 2

When lights come back up, the scene is a similar living room. JOSH is sitting on the couch with a gun to his head. He's hesitant. He puts the gun down, gets up, writes something on a piece of paper and puts it next to a fishbowl on a table. Sits back down, steels himself and prepares to pull the trigger. Doorbell rings. JOSH – surprised – gets up, looks around and stashes the gun in a drawer. He goes to the door.

KATELYN

(pushing her way in) Hey! Happy Birthday!

The other GUESTS rush in, ALEXA bringing up the rear.

LOUIS

(slapping him on the back) Happy Birthday Josh!

KATELYN

(looking around a little disgusted with the place) You're Josh?

JOSH

(hesitantly) Yes.

KATELYN

(shoving the cake at him) Happy Birthday.

LOUIS plops down on the couch. The others throw the stuff down on a table. ALEXA is looking around the room nonchalantly. She spies the gun in the partially open drawer. She surreptitiously reads the note without picking it up. No one else notices. They are looking at JOSH who turns to look at each of them.

JOSH

Who are you people?

LOUIS

(as if Josh should know him) Louis. Louis Messersmith. Remember? Drunk driving class?

JOSH

(Blank stare, then finally speaking) Drunk driving class, right.

LOUIS

(popping some chips in his mouth) Did you get your license back?

JOSH

Uh. Yeah. That was two years ago.

JOSH turns around to look at the guests again, confused.

LOUIS

That's great. *(pause)* Well, happy birthday dude.

JOSH

How did you know it was my birthday?

LOUIS

Facebook.

JOSH

Oh.

LOUIS

Got any beer?

JOSH

Uh. Yeah. In the fridge *(he points stage left)*

LOUIS exits and comes back with 2 six packs, puts them on the table after grabbing a beer for himself.

JOSH

Is this like a – drunk driver's reunion or something?

JEREMY

No. It's a – Birthday crawl.

JOSH

That's a thing?

LOUIS

Sure.

Guests mill around, grabbing beers and chips, laughing. ALEXA goes up to JOSH. He's still a little dazed.

ALEXA

You weren't exactly planning on celebrating were you?

JOSH

No. Actually, I hate birthdays.

ALEXA

Hmm. That would explain the gun? *(she points to the drawer)* And the note?

ALEXA retrieves the gun from the drawer and puts it on the tabletop.

JOSH

Oh... Well.

ALEXA

You were planning on a big send off – huh?

JOSH

Is this like an intervention or something?

ALEXA

No! It was supposed to be my surprise party but it's not my birthday and so these clowns – my co-workers – decided to surprise you instead. Just bad timing for you I guess.

JOSH

Yeah.

ALEXA

Here's a riddle. What's worse than spending your birthday alone with a loaded gun?

JOSH

What?

ALEXA

A bunch of idiots paying a surprise birthday visit on you.

JOSH

It's not so bad actually. It's like I suddenly have a whole lot
of friends.

LOUIS

Let's get out of here.

JEREMY

Where do you wanna go?

LOUIS

(inspired) Karaoke!

KATELYN

It's Tuesday! Come on.

The guests all get up to leave. They head for the door – completely ignoring Alexa and Josh. At the door, LOUIS turns around as if his suddenly remembered them.. Instead he runs back, grabs the beer and dashes out the door. We hear them all outside being rowdy.

LOUIS

Par-ty! Come on Jeremy.

KATELYN

Who's driving?

LOUIS

We can take my car but someone's gotta blow in the breath-alyzer for me.

ALEXA

There go your friends.

JOSH

So I guess you're going too?

ALEXA

I'd like to. Go home and look for my cat that is.

JOSH

Well. Thanks for coming.

ALEXA

(sarcastic) Sure. I had a lovely time. (annoyed) I can't very well go and leave you all alone now, can I?

JOSH shrugs his shoulders.

ALEXA

No. I can't. I wouldn't feel very good about myself if I did.

There's a long pause with ALEXA and JOSH just sitting on the couch, both uncomfortable. JOSH gives ALEXA an awkward little smile at one point. She just looks away.

ALEXA

So, you still planning on killing yourself?

JOSH

I don't know. I'm not so sure now.

ALEXA

That *is* the question.

JOSH

Huh?

ALEXA

To be or not to be.

JOSH

Oh.

ALEXA

Should we flip a coin?

JOSH

What do you think?

ALEXA

(*shoulder shrug*) Well, Hamlet decided on life but he ended up dead after all. So – maybe you'll get lucky and just drop dead – or get hit by a car. People don't generally think too kindly of suicides.

JOSH

People don't like me anyway.

ALEXA

They will if you get hit by a car. Or, best case scenario, you get murdered. That's guaranteed popularity. Everyone you ever met will claim they were a close friend. Katelyn will be making all kinds of phone calls.

JOSH

Who's Katelyn?

ALEXA

One of your new friends. Who's now drinking your beer on the way to karaoke.

JOSH

Oh – right.

ALEXA takes a long look at JOSH.

ALEXA

So you've got no friends, is that what this is all about?

JOSH

Yeah. Well, that's part of it.

ALEXA

Boo hoo! Guess what? I've got no friends either. And I'm not putting a gun to my head.

JOSH

You've got plenty of friends.

ALEXA

Those fools? (*she points at the cake*) They didn't even get my name right on the cake. It's not Alicia. It's Alexa. I've been working with them for a year now and not one of them knows anything about me. And, in case you hadn't noticed, they didn't invite me to karaoke either.

JOSH

Did you want to go?

ALEXA

Of course not! And my feelings aren't hurt that they didn't ask me. I'm just glad they're gone.

JOSH

(pause) You want something to eat?

ALEXA

No! I want you to tell me that you're not going to kill yourself after I leave here.

JOSH

Well. I might.

ALEXA

Great. OK. Sit down.

They sit on the couch. ALEXA scrutinizes him.

ALEXA

So you've got no friends? *(he shakes his head no)* No girl-friend – or boyfriend? *(shakes his head no)* You hate your job? *(shakes head yes)* Family?

JOSH

All dead.

ALEXA

Ok. Me *(counting up fingers)* Divorced. One brother who I can't stand. Shitty job. I moved to this town for the shitty job. I've lived here a year and I don't have a single friend.

JOSH

You have a cat.

ALEXA

Not so sure about that either. But the fact is, I'm fine with all that. And I'm not contemplating suicide. How old are you?

JOSH

40

ALEXA

I'm 45. See, my life is worse. Plus, I'm a woman. After 30 women have to start counting in dog years. So I'm like – 90. To your 40.

JOSH

(*pause*) Wanna go out?

ALEXA

No! I don't wanna go out with you. You've got some – serious issues obviously. I don't even want to spend the rest of this evening with you – but I've really got no choice. Look. If you want to kill yourself, this really isn't the way. You need – a little more preparation.

JOSH

What kind of preparation? I bought the gun. I left the note.

ALEXA

This is your suicide note? (*grabbing paper*) Please feed my fish?

JOSH

They're the only creatures on earth who really care about me.

ALEXA

I'm lookin' at them Josh and I don't think they really care. I think that if some of your brains had flown into their bowl they would have eaten them.

JOSH

That's kind of harsh Alexa.

ALEXA

Reality Josh. Reality. It's what we're stuck with. Do you even have a will?

JOSH

No.

ALEXA

Well, there you go. Who's gonna get your stuff after you blow your brains out? Some distant cousin probably.

JOSH

(thinking) That would suck. I hate my cousins.

ALEXA

See? You gotta make out a will. Leave everything to some charity. A – goldfish rescue society or something. Do you have anything to leave?

JOSH

I've got half a million dollars.

ALEXA

What? And you're gonna kill yourself?

JOSH

What good is money, when that's all you've got?

ALEXA

I can't believe you Josh. I figured you were unemployed –
and in debt.

JOSH

Because I was gonna kill myself?

ALEXA

No. Because Louis said you were a loser.

JOSH

(bummed out) Oh. *(inspired)* Hey! I could leave the
money to you.

ALEXA

Oh no. No. No. I think that would be considered a conflict of interest. I'm supposed to be talking you *out* of killing yourself. That would be kind of stupid of me if you were worth half a million to me dead.

JOSH

Maybe I should leave the money to Louis. (*shrugging shoulders*) He remembered my birthday.

ALEXA

I'll kill you myself before I let you do that. Let's think. Why don't you just spend all of the money and *then* kill yourself. Have a little fun. If I had half a million dollars and a death wish I would take a trip around the world. Yeah. Travel, spend all the money and then come home and kill yourself. No. Kill yourself in Venice or St. Petersburg or somewhere more romantic than Milford, Connecticut.

JOSH

You know what's funny?

ALEXA

The fact that your suicide note will probably make it onto some online list of lame suicide notes. Feed my fish. Your legacy. Immortal last words. The cops will get a good laugh. While they're flushing your fish down the toilet.

JOSH

No. That's not what I meant. What's funny is – I *was* actually thinking about using the money to travel. But I really don't want to go alone. I think I'd be lonely. And get depressed.

ALEXA

Depressed? (*holding up the gun*) Hell-lo! Look with a half a million dollars I'm sure you could get someone to go with you.

JOSH

Hey! You could go with me.

ALEXA

Oh no.

JOSH

Why not? You've got no family, no relationship, crappy job. What have you got to lose? Come with me.

ALEXA

Look. That's not where I was going with all that. And – no. No. You're looking for a girlfriend. I'm not gonna be your girlfriend.

JOSH

I don't want you to be my girlfriend.

ALEXA

Then why did you ask me out?

JOSH

(*shrugging shoulders*) Just grasping at straws I guess.

ALEXA

(*unconvinced*) Really?

JOSH

Yeah. I don't find you all that attractive.

ALEXA

So, if I went with you, you wouldn't hit on me?

JOSH

No.

ALEXA

Or get all romantic and think – hey life is great. I've got a girlfriend & money and here I am in Europe.

JOSH

No. I mean – not the girlfriend part. You're definitely not my type.

ALEXA

All right. I get it. *(looking a little skeptical)* And you'll definitely kill yourself when the money's all gone?

JOSH

Well, yeah. I mean then I'll be friendless *and* broke, unemployed and homeless.

ALEXA

Well, leave enough money for some sort of decent burial.

JOSH

You're right.

ALEXA

Yeah I'm right. I'm practical, unlike you.

JOSH

OK. I'll let you make the funeral arrangements.

ALEXA

OK

JOSH

OK

Long pause

JOSH

Can we eat the cake?

ALEXA

(shrugging shoulders) It's your birthday.

**BLACKOUT
THE END**

✳ Pizza Rat

CAST

JOE
ALEX
LILLIAN

JOE and ALEX are at JOE's apartment. ALEX is looking at a couple of JOE's scripts.

ALEX

I don't know. They're both good but...

JOE

But what?

ALEX

Both are good but – you know. They aren't the kind of plays that get in to these festivals. People want relevance. Issue plays. It's the trend. There's so much going on in the world. Write about stories from the news. Immigration, the MeToo movement, white supremacy. There's so much great material. That's what audiences want. I mean, maybe they do. But more importantly, that's what producers want. They're all looking to make the world a better, kinder, more open minded place. Or at least make it seem like they're enlightened.

JOE

I don't know. That's not what I write. That kind of thing.

ALEX

Well, do you want to get into the festival or do you want to keep writing stuff that goes nowhere?

JOE

I don't know – maybe. I'll think about it.

The next day. Same setting. Alex is looking at another script.

JOE

Well, will you be in my play?

ALEX

(*Looking at the script*) Pizza Rat?

JOE

I took your advice and based it on an incident in the news.

ALEX

Pizza Rat is not news. He was a Twitter phenomenon. A joke.

JOE

There's a lot more to the story than just a rat hauling a slice of pizza.

ALEX

No. There isn't. That's why the video is ten seconds long.

JOE

There is more – to a writer there's always more – the story behind the story. I don't just see a rat struggling to bring food home to his family. I see all of us – wrestling with our daily burdens. I see hope and frustration, determination and thwarted dreams, the trials, the pitfalls, the victories. And ruly, this story says everything about the human condition. There's addiction, depression, cruelty, greed.

ALEX

Sounds uplifting.

JOE

It is. There's also redemption – just read it. (*handing it over*)

ALEX

No. (*handing it back*)

JOE

Then I'll give you the synopsis.

ALEX

Rat climbs down stairs dragging a slice of pizza. The end.

JOE

(*ignoring him*) A homeless man – Mikel – is panhandling by the subway station. A businessman hands him a dollar and walks on. Then, feeling generous, the man heads back, hands Mikel another dollar and says "Get yourself something to eat." Mikel...

ALEX

Mikel? Is he Russian?

JOE

No. (*annoyed, continuing*) $2 is exactly how much more Mikel needs to buy a bottle of bum wine so he starts to head out to the liquor store, but then he stops – thinking about the kindness of the man – and turns around and buys a slice of pizza instead. He sits down on the subway steps and is about to take a bite when an obnoxious teen – Eddie – grabs the pizza. He says "Thanks dude," takes a bite and tosses it down the subway stairs.

ALEX

Where pizza Rat finds it and drags it off.

JOE

NO! Let me finish. Mikel has reached his breaking point. He tried to do the right thing by foregoing the wine in favor of food but life has once again played a cruel trick on him. He puts his head in his hands – despairing. A woman walking by feels sorry for Mikel and hands him $5. He walks back across the street to buy the wine.

ALEX

What's the woman's name?

JOE

Doesn't matter. She's a bit player. Mikel sits back down on the steps and cracks open the wine. Then he sees Pizza Rat with his stolen lunch.

ALEX

Hold on. Is the rat played by a human actor?

JOE

Yes. Of course.

ALEX

So if the rat is human sized is the pizza huge or is it a regular slice?

JOE

I don't know. Maybe both. It doesn't matter.

ALEX

Well it does.

JOE

You just don't get it.

ALEX

Nope. Do you think anyone will?

JOE

Absolutely. A playwright has to trust in the audience's intelligence.

ALEX

OK. Go on.

JOE

Mikel is disgusted. And angry. He yells. " Hey, you lousy thief. You stole my dinner, the least you can do is have a drink with me. Come on fucker." He pours a bit of wine into a cup. The rat comes up. He sniffs at the cup of alcohol but won't drink. This is the final straw for Mikel. Despairing he speaks to the audience. "Too toxic even for a sewer rat. That's it. I'm lower than the lowest. Beneath even a subway rat. Go on rat, I'm an unworthy companion. Scram. Get lost." The rat skulks away. The man puts the bottle to his lips.

ALEX

Well, then what? Does he drink himself to death?

JOE

You have to read the rest yourself.

ALEX

Come on.

JOE

No. Here. Take it.

ALEX

I guess. Now I'm curious.

Same setting. One day later

JOE

So you'll do the play?

ALEX

The play is idiotic.

JOE

Well?

ALEX

Do I have to play the rat?

JOE

That's the part I had in mind for you.

ALEX

Maybe if it was a talking rat. Can you give him some lines?

JOE

No! But the rat is the title character. The metaphor for...
for...humanity.

ALEX

I'll do it. But I want a speaking part. I'll play Mikel. IF the play gets accepted.

JOE

Great. Take the script. Do some research.

ALEX

Maybe I should hang out with a homeless person for a day. Spend some time on the subway.

JOE

You're a professional. Do whatever it takes.

A few days later.

JOE

So. Pizza Rat is a go.

ALEX

Congrats.

JOE

I've cast the other parts. First rehearsal Wednesday.

ALEX

I can't believe it – Pizza Rat. Whatta I know I guess.

JOE

I have you to thank for the idea of doing something topical.

ALEX

Not exactly what I had in mind when I gave you that advice.
I still think it's pretty stupid.

JOE

Do you care?

ALEX

Not really.

JOE

Well it made the cut, so the producers obviously liked it.
There was just one problem. I wanted to give the play some
authenticity so I researched which subway station the video
was shot at and I found the closest pizza place and used their
name. The legal team asked the owners for permission and
they said no way, so I had to change it to Three Sisters Pizza.

ALEX

Why would they care? You'd think that would be a pretty
good endorsement for their product. I mean, I'm sure there
was plenty of trash for that rat to choose from. And he certainly made a supreme effort to get it to his lair.

JOE

Rats don't have lairs.

ALEX

What do they have?

JOE

Nests. I guess.

ALEX

Maybe it's holes. Ratholes. Rattraps. No – not rattraps.

JOE

I think the proper term is nest. Rats nest.

ALEX

Right. So what about the subway station? Did you have to
change that?

JOE

No, legal thought that would be OK.

ALEX

Is the rat played by a man or a woman?

JOE

A kind of androgynous woman.

ALEX

Good choice. Sort of the every-rat.

JOE

Wasn't intentional. She just had the best grasp of the character.

ALEX

What about Eddie? You cast that part?

JOE

Actually, I'm going to play Eddie.

ALEX

You're gonna play a teenage boy?

JOE

I had no choice. I'm way over budget. Lillian is equity and that giant slice of pizza cost me more than I expected.

ALEX

Why didn't you just go with a normal size slice?

JOE

I need to do a realistic reenactment of the video – it's the heart of the play. The message is all based on that one act – a slice of urban life.

ALEX

Slice – good one.

JOE

Thanks. That's the subtitle. Pizza Rat – a Slice of Urban Life.

ALEX

Cool. I like it.

JOE

And Lillian is doubling up as the female pedestrian. It'll all work. Don't worry.

ALEX

Well, congrats again. See you Wednesday.

At the short play festival. Midway through Pizza Rat–A Slice of Urban Life. Mikel (Alex dressed as an older homeless man) is sitting on the subway steps. Eddie (Joe wearing a baseball cap, baggy shorts and sneakers, carrying a skateboard in one arm and a bag of Cheetos in the other) – is approaching.

JOE as EDDIE

Hey, sorry about the pizza dude. You hungry? Have some Cheetos.

Awkwardly – juggling the skateboard and some snacks, EDDIE throws a handful of Cheetos at MIKEL then dumps some Skittles on Mikel's head

JOE as EDDIE

Here's some Skittles for dessert!

Eddie skips off down the stairs, clearly amused with himself.

ALEX as MIKEL

What's the point? I'm broken. The end of the line for you Mikel. Might as well drink up. My last dollar, my last bottle, my last night. Cheers (*lifting the bottle to his mouth*)

*PIZZA RAT is climbing up the stairs, dragging
something behind her. She pushes it towards Mikel.
It's a wallet.*

ALEX as MIKEL

What? You stole someone's wallet. For me? No. That's a nice
gesture rat, but it's not right. I can't take stolen goods. But
I'm touched – my little rodent friend. I'll have to see if this
can be returned to its proper owner.

*He digs inside the wallet looking for ID. The rat
has slipped off and then returns with a half bag of
Cheetos which he starts munching. MIKEL pulls
out a drivers license, looks at it and laughs.*

ALEX as MIKEL

Good job rat. Teach that punk a lesson.

*Mikel gives Pizza Rat a high five. He pulls
a wad of bills out of the wallet.*

ALEX as MIKEL

Looks like Christmas to me ratty boy. I can buy me some
first rate hooch with this.

RAT looks at him – disappointed.

ALEX as MIKEL

You might like the good stuff better.

RAT looks sad.

ALEX as MIKEL

Or – I could get myself a hot meal, maybe pick up some decent clothes and see about getting into that shelter on the corner. What do you think rat?

RAT looks up pleased.

ALEX as MIKEL

You know, I don't even really want a drink. Hey, how about some of those Cheetos?

RAT and MIKEL sit together happily munching the Cheetos. End of Pizza Rat play.

Post performance. The theater has emptied out. JOE and ALEX are seated alone in the theater seats.

JOE

I think I saw a couple of people dabbing at their eyes.

ALEX

I teared up a little bit myself.

JOE

I saw that. Nice touch.

ALEX

Thanks. The rat girl was really good. You should use her again.

JOE

I think Lillian would rather be on the winning team next time. She's over there talking to the first prize winners right now.

ALEX

Hey. Winning isn't everything.

JOE

I agree. But I thought it would at least make the top three.

ALEX

Well, that transgender play was pretty good.

JOE

Which one? There were three.

ALEX

First place. Second place was good too.

JOE

Can't believe we didn't get even one vote.

ALEX

What about Lillian's girlfriend?

JOE

She left, right after our play. Pushed her way past a bunch of people. It was awkward.

ALEX

That's probably what set off that mini exodus. Seems like about a lot of people left right after our play.

JOE

Yeah. Well, no one's gonna remember any of the winners a year from now. But Pizza Rat. I think it's pretty memorable.

ALEX

You're right.

JOE

I could have used the prize money though. This thing cost me a fortune.

ALEX

You should have shown the video.

JOE

Legal said no.

ALEX

Right. Hey. I did some more research. You know there's also Avocado Toast Rat in Brooklyn and Taco Squirrel. How about a sequel?

JOE

I said all that I needed to say. Bared my soul. A sequel would be superfluous.

ALEX

Yeah. And probably wouldn't be much of a contender either.

JOE

It's not about winning or losing. The fact is we touched people. We changed lives.

ALEX

Yeah. I think so. Feels good, doesn't it?

JOE

That's why we do what we do.

ALEX

Right on brother.

JOE

Pizza?

ALEX

Sure. Let's get out of here.

JOE and ALEX exit. LILLIAN steps forward.

LILLIAN

The video of the play went viral. I got signed to do a web series. Joe and Alex are now touring around schools with a series of talks on both homelessness and bullying. Two Brothers Pizza attempted – unsuccessfully – to sue Joe. Then they realized that the video was actually helping business and they changed the franchise's name to Pizza Rat. Joe countersued for copyright infringement. But, in the meantime, the Pizza Rat chain declared bankruptcy. Joe's other plays have yet to be produced. He doesn't really care.

BLACKOUT
THE END.

✳ (I'm Dreaming Of) A White Plains Christmas

CAST

BOY – 9 years old
MOTHER
FATHER
SISTER – Teenager
VOLUNTEER
MARIA – Housecleaner

> *9 year old boy is lying in bed. Mother is sitting in a chair next to him.*

MOTHER

(bored) So what do you want for Christmas?

BOY

A working kidney would be nice.

MOTHER

(rolling her eyes) Besides *that*?!

BOY

Well, anything else would be kind of pointless since the doctors don't think I'm gonna make it to Christmas.

MOTHER

Do you have to be such a downer? Can't you show a little Holiday spirit?

BOY

I'll try.

MOTHER

(looking at a notebook) What's the name of your disease again? I want to put it in the Christmas letter.

BOY

It's just kidney failure.

MOTHER

I don't like the word failure. I'll just put cancer. That pretty much covers everything. Well, goodnight. Sweet dreams.

BOY

Good night mother.

Father and mother in the living room.

MOTHER

Look, Timmie's asking for the kidney again. Can't you just let up and buy him one?

FATHER

We've talked about this.

MOTHER

Frank says he's already arranged with a seller in India. It's not like you can't afford it.

FATHER

It turns out that guy already sold one of his kidneys. Greedy fuckers.

MOTHER

So. He's willing to make the ultimate sacrifice for his family.

FATHER

He probably already sold the better one. If I'm gonna pay 20 grand for someone's kidney I want to pick which one.

MOTHER

Well, I'm sure there are plenty of other kidneys for sale in India.

FATHER

Forget it. I'm sticking to my policy of only buying American.

MOTHER

That always costs more. But Frank can probably find you one in Kentucky or somewhere.

FATHER

Look Alison. If I get him the kidney now, next time he's gonna want a liver, then a heart. Where does it stop?

MOTHER

I think it would stop there. At the heart. Why couldn't you have just given him your kidney?

FATHER

Because, if I only have one I'd have to cut down on my drinking and you know that's not gonna happen. Why don't you give him one of yours?

MOTHER

I'm saving mine since it looks like you're probably gonna need one eventually.

FATHER

Well – what about his sister? Why didn't that work out?

MOTHER

She's not a match.

FATHER

That doesn't make sense. Same parents.

MOTHER

(acting cagey) It's just not gonna work – that's all.

FATHER

Oh – I get it.

MOTHER

Well, as long as we're going there. You must have a few other kids kicking around somewhere. I've seen the cancelled checks. Can't you hit one of those mothers up?

FATHER

I'm not giving another penny to any of those vultures or their brats. They're bleeding me dry as it is. Look – he needs to learn to fend for himself. I'm trying to make a man out of him. If he makes it to manhood. He's never been very healthy anyway. Maybe it's time to give up on this one.

SISTER enters

SISTER

I think Timmie's dead.

MOTHER

How do you know?

SISTER

I just walked by his room and he was kind of choking and then making this gurgling sound and then... *(making a dead face)* Nothing.

FATHER

Oh for Christ's sake. I've had enough. I'm going out.

MOTHER

Oh, and leave me here to deal with this.

FATHER

The housekeeper will be here soon. Let her handle it.

FATHER leaves

MOTHER

Great. Just great.

SISTER

Can I have his room?

MOTHER

Aren't you going off to college soon?

SISTER

I'm only 15.

MOTHER

15? Didn't you just have a birthday?

SISTER

Yeah, yesterday. Remember the party? Oh, you probably wouldn't. Well, to refresh your memory, You left with my friends Lincoln and Dylan. Not sure where you three went but we were all happy to see you go.

MOTHER

(remembering fondly) Oh yeah. Anyway, when I was 15 I'd already left home and was making my own way – as a dancer.

SISTER

Dancer, ha! You mean stripper and I'd be fine with that if you had given me the titty job I wanted for my birthday.

MOTHER

OK. OK. You'll get implants for Christmas. Oh. Maybe you can have mine. I'm thinking of going with something smaller and perkier.

SISTER

I don't want hand me down boobs! And besides – yours are so out of style. More natural looking is the way to go now. Nobody gets those blow-up-doll basketballs anymore. Yours are such "mom boobs"

MOTHER

Hey, these "mom boobs" got me this house and everything else we have.

*Doorbell, mother answers door. A man –
a stranger is standing there, smiling.*

VOLUNTEER

Hello. I'm wth the Christmas Fund. We're collecting used toys and clothes for kids in need.

MOTHER

Your timing is perfect. There's a whole bunch of stuff down the hall. Second room on the left. Take whatever you want.

VOLUNTEER

That's very generous. Thank you.

MOTHER

I'm heading out. Just close the front door when you leave. It'll lock behind you.

VOLUNTEER exits towards Timmie's room.

SISTER

I'm not staying here alone. With him.

MOTHER

He looks harmless enough,

SISTER

Not him. I mean *him.*

MOTHER

Oh.

VOLUNTEER comes back out

VOLUNTEER

Excuse me, Um.

MOTHER

(snapping) He's SLEEPING. Don't worry. He doesn't need any of that crap anymore.

VOLUNTEER

OK

VOLUNTEER exits again.

MOTHER

(to sister) Go cover him up with a blanket or something

SISTER

Eww! No.

MOTHER

All right. Do you want to come Christmas shopping with me?

SISTER

Uh. Yeah.

MOTHER

All right. Here's my Christmas list. (*looking at it*) I guess we can scratch that name off.

MARIA enters

MOTHER

Maria. Good. We're just going out. (*starting to leave, then turning back*) Oh, and Maria. Just remember it's your people's favorite time of year. Christmas Bonus Season.

MARIA

Yes Miss.

MOTHER and SISTER exit

*Maria looks confused by mother's comment
as she heads into the apartment*

**BLACKOUT
THE END.**

✳ The Understudy – A Broadway Murder Mystery

CHARACTERS

JASON – the understudy for the lead of a Broadway show.
BRIAN – The second male lead.
CHELSEA – Leading lady.
PIERCE – Supporting Actor.
LAINEY – Supporting Actress.
GRETCHEN – Supporting Actress
DETECTIVE NOLAN
DETECTIVE CLARKSON
PRODUCTION MANAGER
STAGE MANAGER
AGENT

> *JASON is standing on a chair with a noose around his neck. Brian enters*

BRIAN

What are you doing?

JASON

Understudy no longer. I will finally be the star. Of my own little tragedy. Farewell.

BRIAN

That's a one performance gig, man. Get down. Jack's late. Maybe this will be your night.

JASON

No. It won't. Jack always shows. Last week he was late. I got dressed, made up. Ready to go on. Last minute, he comes running in, looking fabulous, as always. Turns out he got mugged on the way to the theater. Beat up. Left unconcious. 5 minutes before curtain, he's not only looking perfect, he had time to help the police catch the mugger. The cops got front row seats. When Jack's mother died, he held the funeral across the street in that abandoned theater so that he could dash over between Sunday shows.

BRIAN

I get the idea.

JASON

It's useless. I'll never set foot on a Broadway stage.

BRIAN

There'll be other shows.

JASON

No. This was my last chance. I swore I'd give up and move back in with my mother if I didn't make it with this show.

BRIAN

You already live with your mother.

JASON

See. There's nowhere to go once you've hit the bottom. Except. Further down*(pointing down)*

BRIAN

Gotcha. Well, it's too bad Jack couldn't just drop dead instead.

JASON

Jack? Jack is immortal.

BRIAN

Well, gotta go. I'm on in five.

Brian exits. Jason talks alound to himself.

JASON

Immortal. I wonder if that's true. Maybe there is another way out. Maybe, I can play the lead, even if it's just for one night.

He takes the noose off from around his head.
Lights. Focus shifts to center stage.
BRIAN, PIERCE, CHELSEA, LAINEY, STAGE
MANAGER and AGENT are gathered.
PRODUCTION MANAGER is making an announcement

PRODUCTION MANAGER

Tonight's show is cancelled. The star is dead. He was murdered. The rest of the run is off.

CHELSEA

Murdered?

PRODUCTION MANAGER

Yep.

CHELSEA

Well, I think we need some answers.

He turns around waiting to hear the questions.

CHELSEA

Do I still get paid if the show gets cancelled?

PRODUCTION MANAGER

Not sure. I think so.

BRIAN

Hold on. If I take on another show, will that void my contract, or can I still collect my wages?

CHELSEA

I had a great audition the other day.

PIERCE

I for one will be glad for some time off. I've worked nonstop all year.

PRODUCTION MANAGER

Talk to your agents. Talk to your union reps. I've got no more information. Jack's dead. Show's off.

The actors mill around comparing their situations.

BRIAN

There's another show I wanted to do anyway.

NOLAN AND CLARKSON enter and walk around, observing the the scene & the actors. No one seems to notice. JASON enters, panting, disheveled, sees the cops, tries to turn around to leave. NOLAN stops him.

NOLAN

Hey you. Wanna ask you a few questions.

JASON

Me. What about?

CLARKSON

We've just discovered the body of Jack Hallenbach.

JASON

Already?

NOLAN

(*suspicious*) Already? (*eyeing him*) Are you questioning my ability as a detective? Becase if so, I want you to know, the NYPD is fast. (*snaps fingers*) Fast.

JASON

I guess so. He was here for the matinee. How did you discover the body?

NOLAN

When he was fifteen mintues late for his Genius Bar appointment, the tech got suspicious.

JASON

Really?

CLARKSON

Jack Hallenbach never missed an appointment.

JASON

Oh. Right.

NOLAN

The tech filed a missing persons report. We put out an APB. Set up a Tipline. Amber Alert. Then we got a break. A hot tip. Someone suggested we check his apartment. We did. He was dead.

JASON

I'm shocked.

NOLAN

(writing in a book) And who are you?

JASON

Jason Menahan.

NOLAN

Never heard of you.

JASON

No. You wouldn't have. I'm Jack's understudy.

NOLAN snaps the book shut. Starts to walk away.

JASON

Didn't you say you wanted to ask me some questions?

NOLAN

The understudy? Nah. No one cares. Which one was his leading lady?

BRIAN

(to Pierce) Upstaged again.

CHELSEA

Just like Jack. Needs all the attention. Look at me. I'm Jack Hallenbach. Guess what. I'm dead. Oh. Better yet. Not just dead – murdered. My name will be in all the papers tomorrow. As always.

BRIAN

I hope they use his old head shot. From before he got the eyelift.

LAINEY

With the blowback?

Actors all laugh

LAINEY

I think I have one of those old ones. I'll give it to the detectives. Do you think they'll want mine too.

CHELSEA

What for?

LAINEY

I don't know. Maybe as a witness... or a suspect... or something.

NOLAN approaches CHELSEA

NOLAN

Are you Chelsea Alcott?

CHELSEA

Yes. *(puts her hand to her chest as in "who me")* Am I a suspect? I don't have an alibi.

The actors try to outdo each other pushing forward
to make their claims for suspicious behavior

BRIAN

I was best friends with the deceased. I *might* have some vital information.

LAINEY

I was Jack's lover. *(everyone looks at her)* His secret lover. And... he might have been cheating on me.

BRIAN

I hated Jack. I wished he would die.

LAINEY

I once said to him, "I'd rather see you dead"

CHELSEA

You said that every night. That was one of your fourteen lines.

LAINEY

Fifteen!

PIERCE

I was his lover's lover. The tip of the love triangle. I insist on speaking with my lawyer.

BRIAN

(*stepping forward*) I'm not signing anything!

LAINEY

I know my rights! I think. (*starting to recite*) You have the right to remain silent (*she falters*)

CHELSEA, BRIAN, PIERCE

Anything you say can and will be used against you...

PRODUCTION MANAGER

(*to detectives*) Every single one of them has been on Law and Order

> *They start quoting their lines from various shows*
> *pacing around in their own little worlds.*

BRIAN

Oh, you'll talk all right

LAINEY

I insist on seeing my lawyer. Immediately.

CHELSEA

You have no idea what I'm capable of

NOLAN

My worst nightmare. They haven't just *seen* the shows... *(raising his voice)* OK. Cut the crap.

PIERCE

(practicing the line. Oblivious that everyone else is silent) OK. Cut the crap. *(tries another delivery)* CUT THE CRAP!

> *PIERCE realizes that everyone else has stopped and the detectives are glaring at him. He stops short.*

CLARKSON

What about the playwright?

ALL

Who cares?

CLARKSON

He could have killed Jack because he didn't like his treatment of the role.

CHELSEA

Ha! He couldn't even *write* a plot that made that much sense. Have you seen this play?

NOLAN

Hold on. None of you are suspects yet.

PRODUCTION MANAGER

And none of them could have done it. They were all at a spinning class at the gym next door.

CLARKSON

All of them?

PRODUCTION MANAGER

All of them. They go every Sunday. The manager lets them in for free. I just talked to him. They're all accounted for.

GRETCHEN enters

GRETCHEN

I wasn't at the spinning class.

NOLAN

Who are you?

GRETCHEN

The female understudy. I don't go to spinning.

LAINEY

Because you're moonlighing with another show. That thing
downtown. The Featherbed or whatever.

GRETCHEN

It's the Featherhead. *(to detectives)* I play the lead.

CLARKSON

OK. So you've got witnesses.

LAINEY

Hah. On a good day maybe.

GRETCHEN

We had a full house today.

CLARKSON

So you've got an alibi.

GRETCHEN

Well...There's an intermission.

CLARKSON

How long is intermission-10 minutes. Not time enough to travel uptown, kill someone and get back.

GRETCHEN

We got a late start to the 2nd half today. Some of the financiers were delayed getting back to their seats.

CLARKSON

But you couldn't have known that would happen.

GRETCHEN

Unless it was a conspiracy.

CHELSEA

You didn't kill Jack. What motive could you possibly have? He wouldn't even have known you if he ran into you on the street waiting outside some shithole theater on a cattle call line, holding a Starbucks cup with your first *and* last name on it.

PIERCE

I know who did it. *(all eyes on him)* The stage manager.

CLARKSON

The stage manager. How do you know?

PIERCE

He's the one person no one would suspect. None of us even knows his name. Bring in the stage manager.

STU

I'm right here.

PIERCE

Oh. I didn't see you.

NOLAN

Where were you earlier this afternoon?

STU

I was out of the country.

NOLAN

When did you get back?

STU

Ten minutes ago.

CLARKSON

When did you leave the country?

STU

Yesterday

CLARKSON

Where were you?

STU

Japan.

CLARKSON

So you went to Japan and turned around and came right back?

STU

I had some sushi but, basically, yes

NOLAN

Why would you do that?

STU

On a bet. Someone told me I couldn't do it.

NOLAN

Someone dared you to do that? But that's insane. Why would you take that bet?

STU

Because I never refuse a dare.

CLARKSON

How much did you bet?

STU

About the price of the airfare. But I did it!

NOLAN

Why would someone ask you to do that?

STU

Why would someone ask me to spend a month living in a giant birdcage with nothing but one of those little swings well, in this case, a big swing, for furniture.

CLARKSON

You did that?

STU

Of course. I'll do anything on a dare.

NOLAN

Hold on. What if someone dared you to kill a man?

STU

I'd probably do it.

CLARKSON

For how much?

STU

(shrugs shoulders) Five grand

NOLAN

Well, I think we've got our man.

CLARKSON

But he was out of the country.

NOLAN

Oh right. You can go. I think I've figured this all out

LAINEY

You have?

NOLAN

Yes. Surrounded by oversized egos, where he can't possibly compete, these dares are what's-his-name's pathetic cry for attention.

CHELSEA

So, he's the murderer?

NOLAN

No. I didn't say I'd solved the murder. Just a little psycho-analysis. Am I right?

STU

Probably. Why else would someone agree to walk into a crack house on a Saturday night and yell "Freeze mother-fuckers" and then say, "Just kidding"

CLARKSON

You did that?

STU

No. That was my idea but they all thought it was too dangerous. I couldn't get anyone to take the bet.

NOLAN

OK. Wacko. You're free to go. I've solved the mystery. It's quite obvious who the killer is.

JASON walks up with his hands together ready to be cuffed.

NOLAN

What are you doing?

JASON

Breaking. You've broken me.

CLARKSON

(to Nolan) Who did *you* think it was?

NOLAN

I was guessing suicide

CLARKSON

But he was stabbed in the back.

NOLAN

A good actor could do that.

PIERCE

I will show you. *(picking up prop knife)* How that's done.

Tries a number of different ways to stab himself in the back. Nothing works. He throws the knife down.

PIERCE

(pointing to Jason) It was him.

CLARKSON

(to Jason) So why'd you do it?

JASON

I murdered Jack so that I could finally get my shot on Broadway.

CLARKSON

But you kind of blew it instead.

JASON

I know. It was a bad plan. And I'm a bad actor.

STU

(to Brian) Not that bad. He fooled the cops.

BRIAN

What would you know?

NOLAN

Well this is no good. A confession. How lame. That won't play out very well for me in the press.

CLARKSON

At least you made the arrest.

NOLAN

I'll hardly get any court time. "Then he came up and said I did it, Thank you detective. You're excused."

CHELSEA

Do you think I'll be called as a witness?

PIERCE

I saw him … doing something … suspicious. I would make a great witness

NOLAN

None of you are going to get a chance to testify. The case will never make it to court. He'll plead guilty and cut a deal. What's up with these confessions? Same thing happened in my last case. Can't anyone be at least a little bit slippery anymore.

CLARKSON

Well, we can hope for the best next time.

NOLAN

No. This was my big chance. I'd already thought of a head-line. Nolan Nabs the Broadway Killer.

CLARKSON

Nabs. What is this the 1940s? Nobody says nabs anymore.

NOLAN

The Post loves alliteration Nolan Nabs. Makes good copy.

CLARKSON

But – You're not exactly a one name detective yet Nolan. Are you?

NOLAN

I could be. But this case won't be my big break. This one's more third page news. "Confession: the Understudy did it."

JASON

Don't you think they'll at least use my name? Or am I des-tined to be "the understudy" forever.

NOLAN

Shut up confessor or I'll shoot you.

CLARKSON

(thinking out loud) Shoot him. That might not be a bad idea. He made a break for it and you had to shoot him. There's a headline in that.

NOLAN

(to Jason) Would you try to escape so that I could shoot you?

STU

(stepping forward) Wait. For $500 I'll run and you can shoot at me. But you only get one shot.

NOLAN

Well that's not gonna make me look very good if I miss

CLARKSON

It'll look worse if you don't miss.

NOLAN

Good point. No it has to be him. *(pointing at Jason)*

JASON

Wait a second..

BRIAN

You were gonna kill yourself anyway. This is your chance to go out in a blaze of glory.

JASON

You're right. I'm never gonna become famous as an actor so why not? Would getting killed by the cops make headlines?

NOLAN

Possibly.

CLARKSON

Possibly? What are you talking about? He's white. And he's actually guilty.

NOLAN

You're right. That *would* be news.

JASON

OK. I'm in.

NOLAN

Start running.

CLARKSON

Wait. I've got an even better idea. Let him go.

NOLAN

Let him go?

CLARKSON

Then if he kills someone else, Bingo! we've got a serial killer on our hands. Front page news for months. TV interviews. Book deal. Miniseries.

NOLAN

Hm. Not bad. *(to Jason)* Would you be willing to kill someone else?

JASON

I guess.

CLARKSON

Could we choose the victim?

JASON

Can I make up my own nickname?

NOLAN

(*shrugs his shoulders*). Sure

JASON

Deal.

*The PRODUCTION MANAGER steps forward
holding a newspaper as if he's reading it. He folds
the paper back with just the front page to the
audience. Then turns it showing the other pages*

**The Leading Man Strikes Again!
Could He Have an Accomplice?
No. It's a One Man Show.**

**BLACKOUT
END OF PLAY.**

✹ Somewhere in the Bronx

CHARACTERS

DAVID – Man in his twenties
JEREMY – Dog

Scene I

DAVID is sitting in a chair facing the window – looking out. On the table is a plate with a half eaten sandwich. David doesn't see JEREMY – a dog enter. Dog starts pawing at a trash can, eventually knocking it over. Startled David turns around.

DAVID

What the fuck. What are you doing here? Oh. I know – you're the mutt from down the hall. Get out! How the hell did you get in here?

JEREMY

(after a pause) You left the door open a crack.

DAVID

What? Wait a second. You can talk? Hold on.

JEREMY

Well, sort of. I mean I can communicate with some people. You obviously.

DAVID

What do you want?

JEREMY

I was hoping for a snack of some sort..

DAVID

Damn scrounging rat. Go home if you're hungry.

JEREMY

They're always forgetting to feed me. Look, anything will do. A scrap of bread. Anything really.

DAVID

All right. You can have the rest of this sandwich.

JEREMY

Bless you.

DAVID

All right, you got what you came for, now get out. I said get out.

Dog turns to leave, then turns back

JEREMY

I thought you might like some company. Someone to talk to.

DAVID

I don't talk to dogs.

JEREMY

Uh huh.

DAVID

What's that supposed to mean?

JEREMY

I know of a dog that you talk to.

DAVID

I don't talk to dogs.

JEREMY

Maybe not dogs plural. But I know you talk to Harvey.

DAVID

Harvey?

JEREMY

Sam's dog. Sam across the way.

DAVID

I know who Sam is.

JEREMY

And you're very well acquainted with Harvey too.

DAVID

I don't know what you're talking about.

JEREMY

Harvey and you are close. Quite close in fact. He's been telling you all kinds of things.

DAVID

What would you know?

JEREMY

I talk to Harvey. He's told me all about you. About your conversations.

DAVID

Harvey told you?

JEREMY

Yep.

DAVID

What exactly did he tell you?

JEREMY

That he's been giving you instructions. He's got you convinced that he's some sort of demon.

DAVID

Not a demon.

JEREMY

No. Then what?

DAVID

You wouldn't understand

JEREMY

Try me.

DAVID

(*pause*) Harvey is *possessed* by a demon.

JEREMY

There's a difference?

DAVID

Yes. It's a 6,000 year old demon who's giving the orders.

JEREMY

Harvey told you that he's 6,000 years old. Ha! He's 3, maybe 3 and a half.

DAVID

Not Harvey! The demon. Look you wouldn't get it.

JEREMY

Oh I get it all right. Harvey's a liar. He lies all the time. About everything.

DAVID

You're the liar!

JEREMY

Who you gonna believe? Some stupid mutt...

DAVID

He's not a mutt. He's a Labrador retriever.

JEREMY

Another lie.

DAVID

Shut up – you pampered poodle.

JEREMY

I'm not a poodle! I'm a Yorkie.

DAVID

A what?

JEREMY

A Yorkie. A full bred Yorkshire Terrier.

DAVID

Same thing. Some sort of glorified poodle. You're not even a dog at all.

JEREMY

I am a dog.

DAVID

You're not. A dog is a proud, brave, loyal beast. You're a poor imitation. A scrawny monkey faced aberration. They bred all of the canine out of you long ago. Shrunk you down. Gave you the hair of a little girl. Long silky hair so that people would stroke you. A dog isn't for stroking. A dog is a fighter, a defender, a guard. Not a puny girly poodle.

JEREMY

Are you done?

DAVID

I could go on.

JEREMY

Don't let me stop you.

DAVID

Monkey face.

JEREMY

Look. You're no god on earth yourself. Look at that belly. That weak chin. Those droopy eyes. You want to call me names and you call yourself a man. You're lazy and spineless.

DAVID

Spineless, eh? If you only knew what I'm capable of. If you only knew what....

JEREMY

I know. I do know. I know more than you realize.

DAVID

You know what?

JEREMY

What you've been up to. What you've been talking to Harvey about.

DAVID

You don't know shit.

JEREMY

Oh no? You're not the only one Harvey's been talking to. I know all your secrets.

DAVID

I got no secrets.

JEREMY

No? I know that Harvey's been talking you into doing things.

DAVID

What are you talking about?

JEREMY

Shooting people. Staging some sort of vendetta.

DAVID

You don't know what you're talking about. Harvey wouldn't talk to you. About anything. You – you're in a whole different class. Harvey wouldn't tell you if I swatted a fly. Why would he?

JEREMY

He's a braggart. He's trying to impress me. And I'm not impressed. With him – or you. Especially you. Killing people. Why David? Because you can't get a woman. Guess what? Neither can I. I got no balls – literally. You're a dupe Berkowitz. A dupe for a damn dog. A butt sniffing, ball licking, couch humping dog.

DAVID

Shut up, Snowball.

JEREMY

Jeremy.

DAVID

Get out of here.

JEREMY

Don't you want to hear what else I know?

DAVID

You don't know shit.

JEREMY

OK.

DAVID

All right. So what do you think you know?

JEREMY

I know that Harvey's got you convinced that he's the devil.

DAVID

Not the devil! I told you – he's possessed by a demon. It's not Harvey who's talking. Whose commands I follow. It's the incarnation of an ancient demon.

JEREMY

Right – sucker. And Harvey's not going to the electric chair. You are.

DAVID

There's no death penalty in New York, fool.

JEREMY

OK. Life behind bars. While Harvey leads the life of a spoiled pet – laughing at you.

DAVID

I'm not gonna get caught. I'm too smart for that.

JEREMY

Too smart? You're an idiot David. What are you doing all of this for? For Harvey, or Harvey's demon? No. You're trying to get revenge on all of the women who wouldn't have anything to do with you.

DAVID

That's bullshit. Don't try to psychoanalyze me.

JEREMY

You know David. You're not a bad looking guy. Lose a few pounds, shave regularly. If you were really so smart you'd work on some self improvement so you could get laid.

DAVID

What would you know? You eunuch.

JEREMY

Seems like you have no balls either David.

DAVID

Oh no? You think it doesn't take balls to shoot someone. You think it doesn't take balls to walk up to a car, pull the trigger and then walk nonchalantly away?

JEREMY

No. I don't think so. I think that scenario takes a total lack of balls. You couldn't approach a woman without a gun in your hand, without sneaking up on her, without saying absolutely nothing and not letting her see your face. Just venting some misplaced anger. That's total cowardly bullshit.

DAVID

Shut up. Just shut up! And get the hell out of here. I'm not taking advice from any flea bitten mongrel.

JEREMY

I wouldn't expect you to.

DAVID

Then what are you doing wasting my time.

JEREMY

I wouldn't expect you to listen to anything I have to say. You know why?

DAVID

No. Tell me. Why?

JEREMY

Because dog's can't talk.

DAVID

Oh. That's funny. Really funny. You're a talking dog telling me that dog's can't talk.

JEREMY

No. David. I'm not a talking dog. Harvey's not a talking dog. We're both just dogs.

DAVID

What the hell do you mean?

JEREMY

I can't talk David. Harvey may be a pain in the ass with his barking, but he can't talk either.

DAVID

This is bullshit. You're talking to me right now.

JEREMY

I am?

DAVID

Yes. And Harvey talks to me – almost every night.

JEREMY

Harvey's never been in this apartment.

DAVID

He doesn't have to physically be here. He talks through the walls.

JEREMY

Right.

DAVID

Why am I bothering with you at all?

JEREMY

I don't know. Why are you?

DAVID

Because I felt sorry for you. You were hungry.

JEREMY

Maybe because you see a little bit of yourself in me.

DAVID

HA! That's a joke. You're weak and annoying and your own people neglect you.

JEREMY

Right.

DAVID

What's that supposed to mean.

JEREMY

Nothing – really.

DAVID

Look, a minute ago you told me that you can't talk. So – why don't you just get out. I fed you. Leave.

JEREMY

I'm going. Give you some time to think about our "conversation"

DAVID

That never happened according to you.

JEREMY

That's right, David. You didn't have a conversation with a dog. You never talked to Harvey or me. Well, maybe you do talk to Harvey, but he doesn't answer you. Even if he could understand what you're saying, he couldn't hear you across the courtyard.

DAVID

Look Snowflake. You're pushing me. I might just have to hurt you.

*Dog barking. David is startled, then attentive
to the barks, looking out window.*

JEREMY

What is it David?

DAVID

Shh.

JEREMY

Is that Harvey? Talking to you? Telling you to do things?

DAVID

Shut the hell up.

No response from Jeremy.

DAVID

Stop looking at me! Get the hell out! Damn mongrel. Out! Out!

JEREMY looks cowed. Puts head down and slinks off stage.

DAVID

That little shit. Comes over here and tries to tell me I'm crazy or something.

More barking.

DAVID

Sam. Master. I'm sorry. I'm listening now. What do you want me to do?

More barking.

BLACKOUT
THE END

✳ **The Other Side**

CHARACTERS

CHICKEN
FOX
RABBIT
TURTLE
HUNTER
GOOSE
FARMER

SCENE 1

Setting: On stage right is a stepladder representing a fence with some bunches of grapes hanging down from the top. On stage left is a large rock. Centerstage, upstage is a bush.

At Rise: Stage is unoccupied.

> (*CHICKEN runs across from stage left to stage right, offstage and back again.*)

CHICKEN

The sky is falling! The sky is falling!

*(CHICKEN stops mid stage on her second
entrance and addresses the audience.)*

CHICKEN

Really. Really. It is. Nobody believes me.

(FOX enters stage left strolling casually)

FOX

I believe you.

CHICKEN

(screeches) You're going to eat me aren't you?

FOX

Eat you? No. I'm a vegetarian. I'm actually more interested
in those grapes up there.

CHICKEN

Really?

FOX

Really.

CHICKEN

You know the sky is falling?

FOX

So I heard. Well, look, until that happens I was thinking maybe you could help me.

CHICKEN

Me?

FOX

Yes. You see I can't quite reach the grapes and I was thinking that you could fly up and grab them for me.

CHICKEN

Me?

FOX

Yeah, you're a bird

CHICKEN

Sort of. I mean chickens aren't very good at flying.

FOX

You got wings. Come on. Just give it a try.

*(CHICKEN flaps her wings a few
times but can't get airborne.)*

FOX

I'm sure they're sour anyway.

(FOX starts to walk away, then stops and turns back)

FOX

I'm pretty hungry though. Hm. I might have to rethink this vegetarian thing.

*(CHICKEN jumps in fear. She flaps furiously.
Then, in slow motion – flapping arms – she
climbs the stepladder to the top as if flying.)*

FOX

I was only kidding. But as long as you're up there...

*(FOX is interrupted when RABBIT races across the stage
from stage right. She runs back and forth a few times, FOX
and CHICKEN watch – heads back and forth. TURTLE
with a walker enters stage right walking very slowly.)*

TURTLE

Oy vey. I'm tired.

(RABBIT runs circles around TURTLE.
FOX is looking hungrily at RABBIT.)

FOX

I do sometimes miss rabbit. That – and bacon. But rabbit, ummm!

CHICKEN

NO!

(Thinking fast CHICKEN tosses the grapes
down. FOX pounces on them.)

CHICKEN

Run rabbit!

RABBIT

Uh. That's what I've *been* doing. Thanks for the encouragement though.

CHICKEN

No. Forget the race. I mean run before the fox gets you.

FOX

I'm good. These grapes are delicious after all.

*(RABBIT picks up running in circles again. She's
so busy that she doesn't see TURTLE reach the
finish line – the rock. Very slowly TURTLE turns
around and slowly raises his arms up in victory.)*

TURTLE

I won! I won!

RABBIT

This happens to me every time. *(to chicken)* You distracted me.

CHICKEN

I saved your hide. The fox was gonna eat you. The sky is falling by the way.

RABBIT

That's just a conspiracy theory.

TURTLE

Uh. Can you explain something to me. Why were we doing this again?

RABBIT

To prove a point.

TURTLE

And the point is?

RABBIT

Um? That a rabbit is faster than a turtle?

TURTLE

Oy! What a waste of time. I'm exhausted. And starving. And now I have to walk all the way back to the pond.

FOX

Sit. Relax. Have some grapes.

TURTLE

Don't mind if I do. Umm. These are pretty good.

RABBIT

I'll race you back.

TURTLE

Are you crazy? I'll be lucky if I don't have a coronary and die on the spot.

(HUNTER carrying a rifle enters stage right. He stops midstage. Turning to each as he points the gun at them.)

HUNTER

Hmm. Rabbit, turtle or fox?

FOX

Rabbit. Definitely rabbit.

RABBIT

I'm outta here.

(RABBIT runs off stage left. HUNTER looks at FOX.)

FOX

Endangered..... Really.

(HUNTER looks at TURTLE.)

TURTLE

Go ahead. Put me out of my misery. I ache all over and I can't face walking all the way back to the pond.

FOX

Isn't the pond just over there? (pointing) Like maybe 20 yards away? Like really, really close.

TURTLE

Easy for you to say.

HUNTER

Well, I'm not a fan of turtle soup and – really, shooting you wouldn't be much of a challenge.

TURTLE

Hey! I just won a race you know.

FOX

(to HUNTER) Looks like you're out of luck here. Thanks for passing through anyway.

(HUNTER starts to leave. He hadn't noticed CHICKEN on the fence until...)

CHICKEN

The sky is falling!

(All eyes, including HUNTER'S turn to CHICKEN.)

CHICKEN

(very uncertainly) The sky is...

(CHICKEN panics and falls off the fence, right in front of HUNTER. Pause. HUNTER raises his gun.)

HUNTER

Chicken dinner.

TURTLE

Such a tiny, scrawny, little chicken. Is it really worth the trouble?

HUNTER

(pointing gun) Any last words?

CHICKEN

(gulping) The sky is falling?

HUNTER

(lowering gun) What does that even mean? I never got that.

(HUNTER raises gun again)

TURTLE

Look, two birds.

HUNTER

Where?

TURTLE

Over there. In that bush.

(FOX sneaks behind the bush and rattles it. HUNTER looks at CHICKEN, then at the bush, pointing gun in each direction.)

HUNTER

One bird. Two birds.

(HUNTER shoots at the bush multiple times. Bam, bam, bam, bam, bam, bam, bam. (pause) Bam.)

TURTLE

Oh. Too bad. They flew off.

(HUNTER points the gun at CHICKEN who holds up his hands. HUNTER pulls trigger, twice. Out of ammo.)

HUNTER

Not again!

FOX

Live and learn. I'd offer you some grapes but they're really sour.

(HUNTER exits in a huff. CHICKEN puts hands down)

CHICKEN

Phew! This has been a very trying day.

TURTLE

Tell me about it.

(GOOSE enters carrying two huge golden eggs, looks around nervously. Jumps when she sees the others.)

GOOSE

Oh my God! You scared me half to death.

FOX

What've you got there?

GOOSE

(trying to hide eggs under her wings) Nothing.

FOX

Looks like gold to me. You stole them didn't you?

GOOSE

Well, sort of. The farmer was gonna cook me up for Sunday dinner and I needed to convince him that I was more valuable alive. So, I melted down some gold jewelry of his wife's and made these eggs.

TURTLE

Good plan.

GOOSE

Yeah. Except now they expect me to lay golden eggs every day and – this is all I got. The farmer was gonna kill me if I couldn't produce so I grabbed the eggs and ran.

FOX

Why'd you take the eggs? Won't they slow you down? Plus now the farmer is sure to come after you.

GOOSE

OK. I didn't think this out very well but these eggs were a lot of work and – I thought they might come in handy.

(GOOSE looks around nervously)

GOOSE

Could you hide these for me until I can come back for them?

TURTLE

We'll do that IF we can keep one of the eggs.

CHICKEN

Don't do it! That'll make us accessories

TURTLE

Shut your beak chicken.

FOX

(sarcastically) Yeah. Once the sky falls it really won't make much difference will it?

GOOSE

I heard that about the sky falling. Is that true?

TURTLE

Of course you heard it. This chicken won't shut up about it.

(RABBIT runs in racing around in circles again.)

FOX

Who are you racing this time, a sloth?

TURTLE

Or maybe a caterpillar?

GOOSE

A slug?

FOX

Good one.

RABBIT

Very funny. You know I could outrun all of you any day of the week.

FOX

No one's disputing that. What is it it you're trying to prove? Low self esteem?

RABBIT

Well, I don't have much else going for me besides speed.

GOOSE

You're all cute and fuzzy and all.

RABBIT

Really?

(They all nod and make various comments.)

ALL

"Pretty damn cute." "And fuzzy." "Really fuzzy"

RABBIT

Thanks. But I just need to win just this one last race.

FOX

Who was it that agreed to race you this time?

RABBIT

Some farmer. I mean – he was running this way anyway. He seems pissed about something.

GOOSE

(squawking with terror) Take the eggs! I gotta go. The farmer's gonna kill me!

RABBIT

He's pretty fast.

(GOOSE takes off waddling slowly.)

FOX

She doesn't stand a chance.

TURTLE

Hold on. Chicken – get up on the fence.

CHICKEN

That's not as easy as everyone seems to think.

TURTLE

Just do it!

*(CHICKEN makes a supreme effort
and flies up onto the fence.)*

TURTLE

Fox – climb on my shell. Goose – hand him the eggs.

*(FOX climbs up. GOOSE hands the eggs one at a
time to FOX who hoists them up to CHICKEN.
FARMER appears with a butcher knife.)*

FARMER

There you are. You lousy thieving bird.

TURTLE

Now Chicken! Do your thing.

CHICKEN

The sky is falling! The sky is falling!

FARMER (looking around alarmed)

What?

*(CHICKEN drops an egg on FARMER's head.
FARMER is dazed. Rubbing his head.)*

FARMER

It's true after all. I thought that was fake news.

*(CHICKEN drops the other egg. FARMER collapses
dead. RABBIT runs to the rock and touches it.)*

RABBIT

I won. I won. I finally won a race! I usually get all wound up
and run around in circles and blow it but I won this time!

TURTLE

Big deal. You beat a corpse. Look you two, can you help me
back to the pond?

*(FOX and RABBIT take one arm
each and help him offstage.)*

GOOSE

Well, I guess I'll be going too.

CHICKEN

You can hang out here with me.

GOOSE

Only if you cut the shit about the sky falling. For a little
chicken you can be a big pain in the ass.

CHICKEN

What can I say? I'm just the panicky type I guess.

GOOSE

You should work on that. So what do you wanna do?

CHICKEN

There's really not much *to* do around here. I think the boredom is what gets to me.

GOOSE

Well. We've got about fifty pounds of solid gold here. We can go wherever we want.

CHICKEN

I don't know. I like to stay pretty close to home. I get nervous easily.

GOOSE

You think? Come on let's blow this chicken coop.

CHICKEN

I don't know.

GOOSE

Come on. If the sky is gonna fall we might as well have some fun first.

CHICKEN

I guess you're right. Hey! But what if the farmer's wife comes after us? Or if the hunter reloads. Or if the fox changes his diet? Foxes eat geese you know...

GOOSE

Chill Chicken Little. The sky didn't fall – did it?

CHICKEN

Not yet.

GOOSE

It's not gonna fall. And you can't spend your life worrying about what might happen.

CHICKEN

Well, maybe the sky didn't fall but I did wake up this morning with a feeling that something bad was gonna happen. And I was right wasn't I?

GOOSE

It's called a panic attack. Just breathe.

CHICKEN

Breathe. Right. Hey – with all that went on today, do you think we learned anything?

GOOSE

(shrugging) I don't know. Crime *does* pay sometimes?

CHICKEN

Hmm. And what was my lesson?

GOOSE

I don't honestly think you learned anything. I mean – not that you'll listen to me – but it would be literally impossible for the sky to fall. The earth could fall I guess. But not the sky. So – what exactly were you afraid of?

CHICKEN

I don't know, I guess I was speaking metaphorically.

GOOSE

Right. Look. Let's just get going. These eggs aren't gonna move themselves.

CHICKEN

(inspired) Hey. How about gold is the root of all evil?

GOOSE

Well, I don't know about you – but I'm looking forward to a little evil.

CHICKEN

I'm not sure if it's such a good idea hanging out with you after all.

GOOSE

Lighten up Little. I think you could use some excitement in your life.

CHICKEN

Hey. Did you see me fly?

GOOSE

I did. Not bad. Come on. Let's get rolling.

(GOOSE is rolling her egg in front of her. CHICKEN starts walking backwards pulling the egg behind her.)

GOOSE

Not like that!

CHICKEN

What?

GOOSE

The egg has to come first.

CHICKEN

Why?

GOOSE

Because. That's just the way it is. The egg comes first.

CHICKEN

Says who? I'm doing it my way.

GOOSE

Suit yourself. Let's just get a move on and cash these babies in.

CHICKEN

(thinking) Hey. Do we have to cross a road to get there?

GOOSE

Yeah. Why?

CHICKEN

Well, Why do we have to cross the road?

GOOSE

Uh. Can you think of any other way to get where we're going? I mean I know you got up onto the fence and all but I think flying all the way is out of the question.

CHICKEN

No. I understand the *logistics* of crossing the road, I'm just wondering – why the other side?

GOOSE

Because that, my friend, is where life begins!

BLACKOUT
THE END.

* December 27th

CAST

GEORGE
MARY
Their kids
CODY
DYLAN

AGENT 1
AGENT 2

Living room of a typical suburban home – Christmas morning. Two little boys enter and rush up to the Christmas tree under which are numerous wrapped gifts.

DYLAN

There are so many!

CODY

Which ones are mine?

They start diving in to the gifts. There's a knock on the door.

CODY

Is that Santa?

DYLAN

No stupid. Santa doesn't come in the morning.

AGENT 1

Open up. DHS.

CODY

What's DHS?

AGENT 1

This is the Department of Homeland Security. Open up immediately or we'll be forced to break the door down.

CODY

That doesn't sound like Santa.

DYLAN

You don't know what Santa sounds like.

AGENT 1

Last warning.

CODY

You better open the door.

> DYLAN opens the door. 2 DHS agents,
> guns drawn storm the living room.

AGENT 2

Names.

> Kids just look at each other.

AGENT 2

Names!

AGENT 1

They don't speak English. Foreign agents.

AGENT 2

(slowly) What – are – your – names?

DYLAN

Dylan (looking at his brother) and Cody.

AGENT 1

Back up. Come on. Up against the wall.

> *KIDS comply, standing against the wall.*
> *The agents move towards the tree.*

AGENT 2

Where did these come from?

> *KIDS are frightened. They don't answer*

AGENT 2

Did you put these here?

CODY

No.

AGENT 1

No? So you're telling us they just "appeared"

CODY

Yeah.

AGENT 1

You didn't see who put them here?

CODY

No.

AGENT 2

Which one of you made the call?

No answer.

AGENT 2

The call. Who called?

DYLAN

I did.

AGENT 1

And you don't know anything about the packages? They just appeared?

DYLAN

Yes.

CODY

They're from Santa.

AGENT 1

Did I ask you? I'm not talking to you. I'm talking to him. When I want to hear from you, I'll ask.

AGENT 2

Is there anyone else in the house?

DYLAN

My mom and dad.

AGENT 2

Where are they?

DYLAN

Upstairs.

AGENT 1

Go check it out.

> *AGENT 2 starts to exit to head upstairs (backstage) DAD enters in pajamas obviously just waking up. AGENT 2 grabs him.*

DAD

What? What's going on?

AGENT 1

We got a call about some packages from an unidentified source.

CODY

They're from Santa.

AGENT 1

I told you to keep your mouth shut!

DAD

A call? A call from who?

AGENT 1

That's none of your business.

DYLAN

I called.

DAD

What?

DYLAN

If you see something, say something. We're supposed to report any suspicious packages.

DAD

There are "suspicious packages" every year.

DYLAN

These are different times Dad.

DAD

Oh for God's sake. These are Christmas presents.

AGENT 2

Where did they come from? From you?

DAD doesn't answer right away. He looks at the kids, who are looking at him expectantly.

DAD

(hesitantly and slightly embarassed) They're from Santa.

AGENT 1

Did you see him put them here?

DAD

No. I was sleeping.

AGENT 1

So you don't know where they came from?

DAD

From – the North Pole.

AGENT 2

Russia.

DAD

No. Not Russia.

AGENT 2

It's part of Russia. Isn't it?

AGENT 1

I think so.

DAD

No, it's not part of Russia. It's actually closer to Denmark. I'll show you.

DAD walks over and tries to reach for a globe.

AGENT 1

Freeze! Up against the wall.

DAD

Dylan. Why would you do this?

AGENT 2 walks over to the table.

AGENT 2

What's this?

DAD

Cookies and milk.

AGENT 2

(*picking up plate*). I don't see any cookies. Just a few crumbs. And there's not much milk either.

AGENT 1

Bag them.

AGENT 2

And these?

DAD

They're Christmas stockings.

AGENT 2

This one smells like chemicals.

AGENT 2 reaches in and takes out a lump of coal.

AGENT 2

What's this?

DAD

Coal. That's my stocking. We – I mean Santa – puts coal in it every year. It's kind of a family joke.

AGENT 1

Bag it. Could be uranium.

DAD

Where would I even get uranium?

AGENT 1

From one of your sources on the North Pole.

CHRISTIAN

You said Rudolph leaves the stocking presents.

AGENT 1

(*snaps fingers and looks at AGENT 2*) Rudolph the Red.

DAD

Nosed reindeer.

AGENT 1

I told you to shut the hell up!

DAD

Look I could explain this all to you if we could just step into the kitchen. Away from the kids.

AGENT 1

Anything you have to say you can say in front of your accuser.

DAD

My accuser? What do you mean?

DYLAN

That would be me.

AGENT 1

Whatever you have to say, let's hear it. Let's ALL hear it. Where did the USPs come from?

DAD

USPs?

AGENT 1

Unclaimed Suspicious Packages.

DAD

From Santa.

AGENT 2

And this "Santa" how did he get in?

DAD

Through the chimney.

AGENT 2

I don't see any chimney. (*to DAD*) Is there a chimney?

DAD

No.

AGENT 2

So, how did Santa get in?

DAD

From the roof.

AGENT 2

The roof? There was someone on the roof?

CODY

Yeah. The reindeer.

AGENT 2

Reindeer?

CODY

You know – Dasher and Dancer and....

AGENT 1

Codenames. I've heard them before. Does the name Blitzen mean anything to you?

CODY

Sure.

AGENT 1

Let's bring in the canine.

CODY

What's a canine?

AGENT 1

I call it a dog.

CODY

Are we getting a dog for Christmas?

DAD

Please don't bring a dog in here. They'll go nuts asking me for a dog. We can't have a dog. Cody is allergic...

AGENT 1

Shut the fuck up!

DAD

Look it's Christmas. You know, Santa, presents.

AGENT 2

Nice try. It's December 27th.

DAD

Right. Well Cody was in the hospital on Christmas day getting his appendix removed so we moved Christmas up a couple of days.

AGENT 1

LIAR!

AGENT 1 grabs Dad's arm.

AGENT 1

Let's go.

AGENT 2 is looking at the packages.

AGENT 2

Who's Hugo?

DAD

The cat. That one's from the cat.

AGENT 1

The cat wrapped up a Christmas present?

DAD

Well, sort of.

CODY

It's not from Hugo?

DAD

Yes. Yes it is.

AGENT 1

Right.

AGENT 2 is examining another package very carefully.

AGENT 2

This one. I'm pretty sure there's a device in here.

DAD

No, it's just …

AGENT 1

Just what?

DAD

Look, if you really think it's some sort of explosive device, why would I blow up my own house?

AGENT 1

So what is it?

DAD

(*pause*) I can't tell you.

AGENT 1

And why is that?

DAD

It's a surprise. (*whispering*) The kids. Can't we just talk in private – without the kids.

AGENT 1 points gun at his head.

AGENT 1

Talk! Right here. Right now. Or there will be consequences.

DAD

All right! It's a Jedi light saber and a stormtrooper blaster. Are you satisfied?

CODY

Cool!

AGENT 2

"Santa" is giving your kids weapons for Christmas?

DAD

They're toys. Thanks a lot. You've ruined Christmas.

AGENT 2

I'd say you ruined Christmas. By moving it up two days. You can't just do that.

AGENT 1

And guess what? I'm gonna really ruin Christmas for you.

AGENT 1 Handcuffs him and leads him towards the door.

AGENT 1

Stay here with the informant and the USPs until the bomb squad comes.

AGENT 2

What about the short guy?

AGENT 1

He may know more than he's letting on. Work him over.

AGENT 1 is pushing DAD out the door.

DAD

(yelling back to kids) Just so you know Cody, your brother is the one who ruined Christmas.

AGENT 1

Shut it! And keep moving!

DAD

Thanks a lot Dylan. And Santa got you an X box. Might as well ruin your surprise too.

Mother enters wearing a robe. She sees what is going on but doesn't really react. Dad looks at her sort of pleadingly before he's pushed offstage. Mother folds her arms.

MOTHER

(shaking head) Typical.

Lights fade. Jingle Bells plays.

AGENT 1 and DAD exit.

AGENT 2

So how old are you guys?

DYLAN

10

CODY

7

AGENT 2

And what are your favorite classes at school?

BLACKOUT
THE END.

✳ Fiction

CHARACTERS

IRWIN
JESSICA

IRWIN sits on a couch reading a book. JESSICA enters.

JESSICA

What are you reading?

IRWIN shows her the cover.

JESSICA

Is it good?

IRWIN

I don't know. I've only read the first couple of chapters.

JESSICA

Would I like it?

IRWIN

No.

JESSICA

Is there a lot of violence?

IRWIN

Not so far.

JESSICA

Too bad.

IRWIN

Right. You wouldn't like it.

JESSICA

Is there a polygamist who has multiple families none of whom know about each other?

IRWIN

No. Not that kind of book.

JESSICA

What kind of book is it?

IRWIN

Not that kind.

JESSICA

Does any of it take place at a circus?

IRWIN tries to ignore her and continue reading.

JESSICA

A haunted shoe factory?

IRWIN keeps reading.

JESSICA

A mental hospital?

IRWIN

(*frustrated*) NO! Well, actually – it's not a mental hospital but one character's father has spent some time in the psych ward.

He reads for a while. She tries to keep quiet.

JESSICA

Is there a character who can't seem to get over the loss of her daughter – even though she died years ago?

IRWIN

No.

JESSICA

Oh. I thought maybe it was that kind of book.

IRWIN

Actually – yes – there is a woman like that, oddly enough.

JESSICA

So she gets a monkey and dresses it up in the child's clothing and drives around with it in a baby's car seat?

IRWIN

No. The daughter was a teenager. Not a baby.

JESSICA

A runaway who becomes a prostitute and winds up the victim of a serial killer?

IRWIN

No. Cancer.

JESSICA

Right.

IRWIN

It's just not that kind of book.

JESSICA

What kind of book is it?

IRWIN

It's – about a variety of people dealing with different forms
of loneliness.

JESSICA

Like the woman whose father is in the mental hospital.

IRWIN

Not a mental hospital. He ends up in the psych ward of a
regular hospital.

JESSICA

Because they find out that he has been collecting Nazi memorabilia and painting pictures in his own blood.

IRWIN

Yeah. That's why.

JESSICA

And strangely enough, the paintings are fairly pedestrian rustic landscapes.

IRWIN

Painted in blood.

JESSICA

Is the daughter the one who lost *her* daughter?

IRWIN

No, that's another character.

JESSICA

So the woman whose father is in the psych ward ends up losing it and she puts her hand in the freezer until all of her fingers get frostbite and have to be amputated.

IRWIN

I don't think that's gonna happen. She's pretty emotionally vacant.

JESSICA

That's why everyone is so surprised.

IRWIN

Right.

JESSICA

And even more surprised when she quits her corporate job to join a heavy metal band as a drummer.

IRWIN

A one handed drummer?

JESSICA

Who sometimes plays topless.

IRWIN

Of course.

JESSICA

And she wears a sort of glove made out of an actual tiger's paw over her mutilated hand.

IRWIN

She plays the drums with the tiger's paw?

JESSICA

No. She plays one handed. The paw is just for show. And as part of the act, she uses the claws to rip off the lead singer's shirt.

IRWIN

Sounds very effective.

JESSICA

And then she climbs between his legs and simulates oral sex.

IRWIN

Who's playing the drums while this is going on?

JESSICA

It's during the guitar solo.

IRWIN

Isn't the guitarist annoyed that they're stealing his thunder during his big moment?.

JESSICA

Yes – and so he kills the lead singer.

IRWIN

By secretly putting poison on the tiger claws so that when she rips off his shirt …

JESSICA

Exactly. Then what happens?

IRWIN

She ends up in the psych ward.

JESSICA

With her father?

IRWIN

No. He's gotten out by this time. His blood paintings have become highly desirable and he's making a fortune.

JESSICA

So he can hire a good lawyer to get her off.

IRWIN

He could, but he's still angry about her getting him committed.

JESSICA

Oh. She's responsible.

IRWIN

Yep. Although he didn't know that until the other woman ...

JESSICA

The one with the chimp.

IRWIN

It's not a chimp. It's a rhesus monkey.

JESSICA

Of course

IRWIN

That woman found out about the daughter committing her father – in order to get all his money

JESSICA

When did she find out?

IRWIN

When she was at the circus – stealing the monkey.

JESSICA

Who told her?

IRWIN

Nobody told her. She overheard the lion tamers discussing it.

JESSICA

How did the lion tamers know the story?

IRWIN

The one handed woman bought the tiger's paw from them and, while she was there, she got drunk with the lion tamers and confessed the whole thing.

JESSICA

Right. So does she end up in jail?

IRWIN

No. She kills herself.

JESSICA

How?

IRWIN

Mauled to death.

JESSICA

Of course. With her own paw. And the other woman?

IRWIN

Turns out it wasn't her daughter who was killed. It was another prostitute.

JESSICA

But I thought the daughter was a baby? Why was the monkey wearing baby clothes?

IRWIN

Because – the mother couldn't very well substitute a monkey for a teenager so, in her disordered mind, she had regressed the daughter to a baby.

JESSICA

And does she freak out when the daughter returns?

IRWIN

Not at all – but she decides that she prefers the monkey.

JESSICA

Well, serves the daughter right for running away.

IRWIN

The daughter ran away because the mother had grown hugely fat and couldn't fit through the door.

JESSICA

But she lost the weight when the daughter died.

IRWIN

Right. And the daughter has gone on to become a successful veterinarian.

JESSICA

Perfect. For a girl with a monkey sister.

IRWIN

The monkey's actually a male. The woman couldn't be too picky when she snuck into the circus. She had to snatch and run.

JESSICA

Does the daughter end up with the other woman's father –
the blood artist?

IRWIN

Of course not. She's one of the polygamist's wives.

JESSICA

I thought you said that there wasn't a polygamist plotline

IRWIN

I misspoke. He's actually just a bigamist. So far at least.

JESSICA

With two homes and two sets of kids?

IRWIN

Naturally.

JESSICA

Does she find out about the secret family?

IRWIN

I haven't gotten that far yet.

JESSICA

All that happened in the first two chapters?

IRWIN

Yep. Which is surprising because the critics called it "relentlessly dull"

JESSICA

I can see that.

IRWIN

Really?

JESSICA

Yeah. Low body count. You're right. I wouldn't like the book.

IRWIN

No. It's crap.

JESSICA

What's it called?

IRWIN

The Winter Rose Garden

JESSICA

Good title.

IRWIN

I'll lend it to you when I'm done.

JESSICA

Great. Read me a little bit. Like the first paragraph.

IRWIN

OK *(reading)* "All that was left of the garden were dead roses on blackened spiky stems and a few dried leaves encased in the frozen mud. Harold stepped outside – his boots made a crunching sound as he walked listlessly among the icebound desolation that was once a source of such great pleasure to him and Marilyn. How she had loved the garden. The hours she spent nursing the roses with the tender devotion of a new mother. Harold sighed and headed back inside – where nothing but an empty house and forlorn memories of happier times awaited him.

JESSICA

Hmm. Slow start. Harold's a bit of a bore. Ooh. But I bet he murdered Marilyn and buried her in the rose garden. Along with some other women.

IRWIN

Nope. She just died in a car accident.

JESSICA

Or so they thought...

IRWIN

Pretty sure it was just a car accident.

JESSICA

Hmm. OK. But I can't wait to find out about the polygamist and the monkey baby.

IRWIN

Right. So let me finish it.

JESSICA

Fine. I've got stuff to do anyway.

JESSICA exits. IRWIN gives a sigh of relief. He picks up the book. Reads for a few seconds. Throws it down and exits.

**BLACKOUT
THE END.**

Poems

Top of the Food Chain Blues

I'm staring at a rat on the subway tracks
She's staring back at me
It's a case of mutual disdain
Well, not really mutual.
I think she's the more disgusted of the two

I'm trying to read what's going on in her tiny rat brain
As best as I can tell, she's feeling superior
Rat: "What's so special about you?
You have to worry about making the rent and paying the bills
Rushing around trying to get to appointments, engage-
ments, assignments, assignations.
You're at the mercy of a tyrannical boss
Plagued by insomnia, anxiety, depression
Obsessed with keeping up with fashion, current events, trends
(she knew me pretty well)

Rat: "I have everything I need right here in my subterra-
nean Eden.
I have a steady supply of food and water and a warm place
to sleep

I don't waste my time thinking – boo hoo – I don't have a mate.

Thirty glorious seconds of shame free sex and I had all I needed from the male of my species

25 rat babies. I nursed them for one month, then booted them out of the nest

I don't ever worry about them. At the very least a couple of them will survive long enough to give me grandchildren and make me virtually immortal.

It was that easy.

The rat is still staring at me

"What are you looking at?" I say out loud, causing a few people to move down to the other end of the platform

"You think your life is so great? What about all of the beauty in the world? What about the gratification of achieving accomplishments and successes in your life? What about friendships? Family? What about art? What about love?"

"What about it?" she sneered. Her beady eyes were glowing with hatred.

Then her look softened a little.

"Hey," she said. "What about that pretzel?"

I could see that she was greedily eying the last uneaten piece that I held in my hand.

"Fuck you rat!" I screamed. "You and your goddamn perfect life."

I really didn't want the rest of the pretzel. I was going to throw it away.

But I stuffed it in my mouth and ate it while she watched. Out of spite.

✱ Walter

I bought a cat today.
I hate him.
So self-satisfied.
And self-reliant.
I wanted needy.
He seemed needy. Came right up to me rubbing his head under my hand.
I hesitated. Is this gonna drive me crazy? Maybe.
I took him anyway.
Now it seems as if his overtures were all a show.
He doesn't like me.
He just wanted to get out of captivity and away from the other cats. Probably hated them too.
He's clearly a misanthrope. And a sadist.

He wasn't the best looking cat. Quite possibly the least attractive.
Maybe that was part of his appeal. I thought he'd need some love.
But he completely ignores me. He hates me.
With intensity. It's quite obvious.

And now I have to clean up his shit. Like an aide in a nursing home.

Except it's seven days a week and I don't get paid.

Did I mention that I don't like cats?

I thought I'd learn to love my cat.

It's apparent now – that's not gonna happen.

And I have to feed him, clean his litter pan, worry about fleas and hairballs.

Hairballs. Regurgitated balls of hair.

Eventually he'll die.

Probably after some horrible illness and a terrifying death bed scene.

And I'll have to dispose of him.

I hate my cat.

And I'm a little scared of him.

I suspect he's one of those cats that seduces you into petting him and then strikes. Viciously.

Cats have razor sharp claws. Like a particularly treacherous cactus – that might attack at any moment.

Cats are very, very cruel.

I've been tricked before.

I think I'll stay as far away from my cat as possible.

I bought a cat because I was looking for companionship – I guess.

But you can't buy friends.

Actually you can. You can buy a dog.

I wanted a dog.

But having a dog makes it difficult to get away.

I have nowhere to go and no means to go anywhere anyway.

I should have gotten a dog.

But I got a cat.
I guess it was selfish of me. I bought a living thing to serve some need of my own.
Sort of like slavery.
I'm a terrible person.
I deserve this punishment.

My cat is:
Smarter, hipper, better looking, more athletic, healthier, cleaner, more well adjusted and *far* more self confident than me.
He makes me hate myself.
I hate myself.
I'm not even good enough for my cat.
But he's stuck with me.
Poor cat.
He must despise me.
I would if I were him.

✳ Octopalypse

A giant alien octopus
Suddenly appeared on the scene
The fearsome creature slithered down the street
Somehow propelling itself on a slime trail like a 15 ton slug
Leaving all eight appendages free
To wreak havoc

It snatched up cars and flung them through the air
Lassoed skyscrapers and pulled them crashing to the ground
Uprooted enormous trees as if they were daisies to be plucked
Snapped huge monuments off from their foundations and tossed them aside casually
Yanked loose a suspension bridge like it was tearing the ribbon from a Christmas present
Wiped out an entire block of buildings with a reckless one arm swipe
Swatted airplanes from the sky like they were annoying buzzing insects
Squashed whole crowds of pedestrians with one lethal tentacle slam
Picked up a baby stroller and shook its tiny occupant into its cavernous gaping mouth as if it were dispensing a tic tac

Panic ensued
People shrieked
And fled in every direction
The monster had 360 degree coverage of the scene

I stood and stared
Fascinated – but not afraid
A woman ran by me, holding her head with both hands, and
screaming hysterically
I sneered at her, "It's not the end of the world,"
"Oh – yeah it is," I said, correcting myself.

THE END!

Thanks!

Mark Forst
Mary Dailey
Alexa Poli-Scheigert
MacIntyre Dixon
B.J. Papas
Robin Riley
Victoria Narayan
Sheree Tams
Amanda Wallace
Holly Nadler
Tina Miller
Bricque Garber
Michael DiPietro
Destiny Bowers
Kate Feiffer
Judy Hickey
Robin Sampson
Dawn Marie Angus
Karen Dutton
Jean Kammer
Andrea Reynolds
Karen Haggard
NAKED ANGELS

The author gives permission to perform any
of the plays free of fees as long as you give me
notice by emailing gwynmca@comcast.net

Or send me praise or money.

Thanks

Made in the USA
Middletown, DE
14 May 2023